"Every believer cares about their friends, f to encounter Jesus, but many lack practical methods for how to actually reach them. Fueled by his own encounter with God and leading his own family and friends to the Lord, Angelo burns with a passion to equip you to live out the Great Commission in a simple, yet powerful way.

"We've known Angelo for close to ten years and have watched him live out what he preaches. I wholeheartedly recommend him, his ministry, and this book. Do what it says and you will see revival break out in a dynamic way through you."

TOM CRANDALL & LESLIE CRANDALL
Director of Young Saints and Overseer of Evangelism at Bethel Church
Redding, California *(Tom)*
Co-Overseer, Bethel School of Supernatural Ministry First-Year Program
Redding, California *(Leslie)*

"I absolutely, wholeheartedly, and enthusiastically recommend this book! Angelo has done an excellent job of bringing opportunity for the supernatural and demonstration of the Gospel into your daily life. Fair warning: If you are a bit like me and enjoy living in your personal bubble, content to get by with kind nods, half-smiles, and the occasional 'hello' as you go about your day, this book will challenge you! However, I fully believe that if you take the time to read, meditate on, and actually do what Angelo lays out in this book, you will be transformed in the span of four weeks. Don't just be a reader, be a doer."

GABE VALENZUELA
Senior Overseer of Bethel School of Supernatural Ministry Second-Year Program

"I have known Angelo Jeanpierre and worked closely with him for more than ten years. Through all those years, I have watched him both share this as a message and live it out in his everyday life. In Matthew 9:36–38, Jesus talks about how the harvest is plentiful and the workers are few. We have been commissioned as believers to be workers in the Great Harvest. Jesus paid the ultimate price so that all mankind would be reconciled to God, and we as believers have been equipped to be instruments of this mighty reconciliation. Angelo begins the book honoring the One who empowers this supernatural lifestyle: The Holy Spirit. As you begin reading, you will feel equipped practically and spiritually to partner with the Spirit of God to go and fulfill the Great Commission, ready to make disciples of Jesus all around you. By giving a focused approach, this book will inspire you to walk in increased risk, the pursuit of God, and a radical conviction that the Gospel is powerful and can be displayed in your life. The impossible will become possible with these daily activations and will activate great faith in you to step out of the boat with Jesus."

HAYLEY BRAUN

Associate Overseer of Bethel School of Supernatural Ministry Online

ACTIVATING
THE
EMPOWERED LIFESTYLE

**HOW TO LEAD YOUR FAMILY AND FRIENDS INTO
AN ENCOUNTER WITH THE LOVE OF JESUS**

ANGELO JEANPIERRE

FOREWORDS BY **BILL JOHNSON & CHRIS OVERSTREET**

ACTIVATING THE EMPOWERED LIFESTYLE
By Angelo Jeanpierre

ISBN: 978-1-7365980-2-3

First Printing July 2021
Printed in the USA

Editing by Karla Dial
Cover Design by Aldren Gamalo & Jonathan McGraw
Layout by Jonathan McGraw

www.angelojeanpierre.com

DEDICATION

To all the believers who have a heart to see their

loved ones encountered by the love of God!

CONTENTS

////////////

///////////

FOREWORD

BILL JOHNSON

Jesus commissioned His disciples—both past and future—to spread the Kingdom of God: "Go therefore and make disciples of all the nations..." (Matthew 28:19). Our mandate hasn't changed. Jesus set the standard for spreading the Gospel, and it begins with the command, "Go."

Angelo Jeanpierre has modeled this standard in his own life, and in the process has equipped thousands of students from the Bethel School of Supernatural Ministry to share the Gospel clearly and effectively. His workbook, *Activating the Empowered Lifestyle,* is a distillation of years of personal experience, encouraging others to step outside their comfort zones when it comes to evangelism. It would be easy for us, as Christians, to stay trapped in the bubble of church activities and fellowship. But if we limit our connection with the world, we can unintentionally excessively insulate ourselves and actually limit the impact of God's grace working within and through us.

Our current culture is nearly obsessed with avoiding pain. And when there is a prevailing culture, the Church must either intentionally choose to live in opposition to the cultural climate or be affected by it. Jesus commissioned us to bring the Gospel—the only answer for the sorrow and brokenness around us. To do that, we have to look for people who are hurting. We have to expose ourselves to the pain and need around us beyond our own circle of friends. Our lives are not our own. When we surrendered to Christ, each one of us became His representatives on the earth. His presence flows in us and must flow out of us. Life doesn't grow in stagnant waters.

As we join our hearts with the cry of the world, we can move confidently forward, knowing that we have answers. In the natural, Matthew 10:16 sounds cruel: "Behold, I send you out as sheep in the midst of wolves. Therefore be wise as serpents and harmless as doves." But the nature of the Kingdom is invasive. Our strength is not in our own power or ability or even our debate skills. Our strength is found in our Shepherd who never leaves us, His Holy Spirit who empowers us, and the purity and wisdom that protect us.

God created humanity for His pleasure, but our initial assignment was to confront the sin and bondage that ensnares people, setting them free through God's love. We don't win someone to Christ through our own reasoning or strength, but through our Christlike servanthood and the love of Jesus. The resting presence of the Lord is what qualifies us for our mission. That doesn't necessarily mean that sharing the Gospel in a way that honors and blesses people is immediately obvious or easy. That's where this book comes in.

Angelo's activations are practical and Spirit-filled. They offer an accessible guide to developing a naturally supernatural lifestyle of evangelism. He not only lays the foundation for healthy, loving evangelism, but also walks the reader through each step, providing challenging exercises and encouragement along the way. He has given an incredible tool to the Body of Christ in this book. I would encourage everyone to use it fully and watch what the Lord does through the obedience of His kids.

In Acts 8, the early Church experienced great persecution, which scattered the disciples out from Jerusalem as they shared the Gospel. Philip traveled down into Samaria to preach about Jesus, and signs and wonders followed. Then, the Bible says, "there was great joy in that city" (Acts 8:8). Scripture doesn't tell us which conversion or exactly which miracle was the tipping point, but we do know that it is possible for one encounter with Jesus to create such a domino effect that an entire city is brought into the joy of the Lord. If it was possible for Philip, it's possible for us here and now. We never know who that individual is going to be, but we can share the Gospel with the confidence that, as we step out in faith to share the goodness of God, the atmosphere of Heaven will enter a city, allowing joy to prevail.

This might be the most practical book I've ever seen on evangelism, which the writer brilliantly calls *the empowered lifestyle.* It's practical and inspirational, all while enabling the reader to do what Jesus commanded us to do. What a glorious combination. I'm excited to see this book released. The impact will certainly be measured only in eternity.

Bill Johnson
Bethel Church, Redding, CA
Author of *Born for Significance* and *The Way of Life*

////////////

FOREWORD

CHRIS OVERSTREET

There is a growing hunger in this generation for the authentic Gospel, and a growing need for it to be expressed through the body of Christ.

Activating the Empowered Lifestyle teaches us how we can reveal the heart of Jesus in our relationships with family, friends, neighbors, and the strangers we meet.

The Kingdom of God expands through people who live and see through faith. It is people who see wherever they go as a mission field to reveal Jesus.

My friend Angelo's desire with this book is to equip individuals to demonstrate Jesus's love and power as a lifestyle.

A lifestyle of risk and faith that gets results, where lives around us are transformed by God, has little to do with our techniques and styles but everything to do with how we partner with the Holy Spirit.

If you're looking for a powerful guide to become effective in sharing your faith, this is a great resource that will assist you.

I have known Angelo for over eighteen years, and I am proud of him for writing this book to help people develop a lifestyle of sharing the Gospel.

Chris Overstreet
Founder of Compassion to Action
Portland, Oregon

HOW TO USE THIS BOOK

What you have to give is extraordinary. It heals hearts, releases hope, and ushers in peace. It quiets storms, comforts pain, restores the broken, and sets captives free. No, I'm not talking about your religious practices, your pastor's sermon or being a good Christian, as good as those things might be. I'm talking about everything the Holy Spirit has touched in your life: your story, your breakthroughs, and your passions, as well as what He has made available to you: the Gospel, compassion, the gifts of the Spirit, the Word of God, and His supernatural kindness.

In Acts 3:6, as Peter and John are walking to the temple to pray, a lame beggar calls out to them, asking for money. Peter and John both look at him, giving the lame man hope for spare change. But then Peter says, "Silver or gold I do not have, but what I do have I give you. In the name of Jesus Christ of Nazareth, walk" (NASB). The next thing you know, the lame man is walking, leaping, and praising God!

I love this story because Peter and John focused on what they had to give, not what they didn't have. Oftentimes in life, when we don't have something to contribute, we disqualify ourselves and disengage from opportunities. But the Kingdom is different. When we contribute what we have, no matter how small, God brings the increase! What Peter and John had to give changed a man's life in one moment. And what they had were the promises of God and the Holy Spirit—the same promises and the same Holy Spirit that have been given to you!

So whether you're a stay-at-home mom, a businessperson, a student, or a pastor, I want you to know that what you have is more than enough to *change the world around you.* And I believe this book will help you do just that—activate the empowered lifestyle.

I'm going to help you make sharing what you have to give practical, fun, and engaging. My heart is to keep this simple, so I've set up two "lanes" of activations for you to release what the Holy Spirit has given you, simultaneously—the *daily activations* in which you intentionally prepare for the Lord to encounter the individual He places on your heart, and *the Weekly Five* in which you spontaneously take risks with the people who cross your path. Both are designed to activate you and bring growth, as well as impact the people around you with the love of God.

DAILY ACTIVATIONS

The daily activations excite me because I believe they will equip you to share the Gospel with those who are most consistently in your lives—your family, your coworkers, your neighbors and friends. Acts 1:8 says, "but you will receive power when the Holy Spirit has come upon you; and you shall be My witnesses both in Jerusalem, and in all Judea and Samaria, and even to the remotest part of the earth" (NASB). My hope is that as you demonstrate God's love with *your* Jerusalem (those closest to you), it will cause a ripple effect that transforms the world around you.

Matthew 7:7-11 says:

> *Ask, and it will be given to you; seek, and you will find; knock, and it will be opened to you. For everyone who asks receives, and he who seeks finds, and to him who knocks it will be opened. Or what man is there among you who, when his son asks for a loaf, will give him a stone? Or if he asks for a fish, he will not give him a snake, will he? If you then, being evil, know how to give good gifts to your children, how much more will your Father who is in heaven give what is good to those who ask Him!* (NASB)

We have an extravagantly good Father in Heaven who wants us to ask Him for good gifts! I would like to say that although these gifts are many times for us, they are also for the people around us. We, as God's children, get the opportunity to ask the Father to pour out His goodness on those we encounter—gifts of healing, salvation, hope, freedom, acceptance, love, and purpose. These gifts unlock hearts and draw people to Him. This is exactly what the daily activations are all about.

For the next month, we are going to focus on one person we can minister to each week. Each of these weeks have been broken down into days which will work as building blocks so that by the end of each week, we can take what the Holy Spirit has given us and share it with the people God has placed on our hearts, confidently.

The daily format for each week is as follows. I encourage you to spend a minimum of 15-20 minutes each day with the Holy Spirit to complete each activation:

Day 1—Compassion Day: The focus for this day is to stir up compassion for the person you are praying for. We often see in the life of Jesus that He was moved with compassion when ministering to people. Compassion is the key to getting the heart of God for someone and seeing Heaven invade that person's life.

Day 2—Word Day: This day is focused on unlocking the power of the Word of God! Psalm 107:20 says, "He sent His word and healed them" (NASB). When you release the promises of God over someone's life, God is faithful to heal, save, and deliver that person. Thus, on Day Two, you're going to ask the Lord for a scripture that you can pray into and share with the person you received compassion for on Day One.

Day 3—Gifts Day: People are just one encounter away from surrendering their lives to Jesus! On this day, you're going to ask the Lord for words of knowledge and prophetic words (and any other revelatory insight), so that the person you've been praying for will taste and see that He is good and encounter Him.

Day 4—Gospel Day: People are hungry for the good news! On this day, you are going to ask the Lord for keys on how to release the Gospel in a personal and impactful way. There is power in the proclamation of the Gospel! I believe that as you pray, prepare, and step out to share it, the Lord will be faithful to show up.

Day 5—Encounter Day: This is the day you release what you have cultivated previously—your compassion, the scriptures, the gifts and keys to preaching the Gospel—so that the person you've been praying for encounters the love of God. Paul said, "My message and my preaching were not in persuasive words of wisdom, but in demonstration of the Spirit and of power" (1 Corinthians 2:4, NASB). This is the day you release that power and share what you've been given!

Day 6—Intercession Day: This is the day you pray into the seeds you sowed on Day Five by asking the Lord for keys to share for your follow-up day tomorrow. James 5:16 says, "The effective prayer of a righteous man can accomplish much" (NASB). No matter what the outcome was on Day Five, when you pray for those you encounter, the Lord brings the increase and breakthrough.

Day 7—Follow-Up Day: Following up is a key to displaying the care and love of the Lord. It's also what discipleship is about. The goal on Day Seven is to connect again with the person you've been praying for—whether by text, phone, or visitation—so you can see how they're doing and share what the Holy Spirit showed you on Day Six.

There is significance in how our words create ecosystems around us that thrive and release life. When we read Genesis, we see that God created a whole ecosystem that thrived in six days. He spoke things into being, and He created. I feel God is inviting us to do the same in our daily lives—to create ecosystems where our loved ones receive life and life abundantly as we speak God's Word over them. In John 7:38, Jesus says, "He who believes in Me, as the Scripture said, 'From his innermost being will flow rivers of living water'" (NASB). I believe that as we drink in the Word of God and speak it, our families, coworkers, and neighbors will receive the outpouring of God's truth and love.

THE WEEKLY FIVE

The Weekly Five are activations that prime us for the "and suddenlies" of life. They teach us to be ready to respond to the Lord in season and out, to be prepared to minister whether we feel like it or not. Just as when Ananias heard the Lord speak to him about ministering to Saul in an instant, we will have opportunities to respond to the Holy Spirit's voice in what might feel like a spontaneous moment. This is what the weekly activations are all about.

For the upcoming weeks, I'm going to encourage you to step out in five ways:

1. **The Prophetic:** The prophetic is a powerful gift because it gives people the opportunity to know that God is still speaking. It also releases life, awakens people to their God-given identities, and sets God's plans in motion. One encounter with a word from the Lord about a person's future can transform that individual's life. In the weeks to come, I challenge you to step out and share God's heart for people, even if what you have to say is simple.

2. **Words of Knowledge:** Unlike prophetic words, which detail future elements of someone's life, words of knowledge are revelations that God gives us to highlight a specific detail about someone's past or present. For instance, God may give us the name of a person's mother, a significant day of their life, or an event that took place in their history. This is powerful because it lets people know that God knows them, sees them, and loves them.

3. **Healing:** Isaiah 53:5 says, "By His stripes we are healed" (NKJV). It is our mandate as believers to carry the healing power of Jesus to those around us. The Greek word for salvation, *sozo,* means "to save, heal, and deliver!" This is what Jesus paid the price for each of us to walk in. When we pray for the sick, we invite Heaven to come and give people the opportunity to experience His love, not just hear about it!

4. **Acts of Kindness and Generosity:** Acts of kindness and generosity are big deals because oftentimes people gain

knowledge about how good God is, but they hesitate to demonstrate it. Acts of kindness can look like leaving an extravagant tip for a server, raking your neighbor's leaves, or blessing someone with a gift card. Romans 2:4 says that His kindness leads us to repentance. By engaging in this activation, we demonstrate His kindness—and that kindness can awaken people to His love!

5.   **The Gospel:** The Gospel is the good news—and the good news is that Jesus, who was perfect and never sinned, redeemed us by taking our punishment and bearing our sins on the cross, thus setting us free! Mark 15:15-16 says, "Go into all the world and preach the Gospel to all creation. He who has believed and has been baptized shall be saved; but he who has disbelieved shall be condemned" (NASB).

Communicating the Gospel is part of the Great Commission Jesus gave us right before He left the earth. Thus, developing how to articulate the Gospel as a lifestyle is one of the greatest things we can do on this side of eternity. I have faith that as you preach the Gospel this month, people's eyes will be opened, hearts will be awakened, and souls will be saved!

HOW TO APPROACH THE WEEKLY FIVE

When you get to the Weekly Five, I would like you to take a moment to ask the Lord to highlight individuals you could minister to. Also, I'd like you to ask Him for courage when you feel prompted to give a prophetic word, stirred to give a word of knowledge, moved to pray for the sick, the compassion to demonstrate His kindness, and/or compelled to share the Gospel.

Again, the goal is for you to respond to the Lord in season and out. As you prepare every day in prayer, I believe the Lord will increase your ability to hear Him and empower you to release the Kingdom of God.

That being said, I encourage you to complete each one of the Weekly Five, every week—those again being *prophecy, words of knowledge, healing, acts of kindness* and *sharing the Gospel*. As you accomplish them, record your testimonies and celebrate your breakthrough! By the end of each week, we will have a debrief to reflect on what God has done and to encourage you!

Here is a sample of what the Weekly Five checklist looks like:

5 WEEKLY FIVE

Check off the activations that you have completed this week.

- ☐ Prophetic
- ☐ Healing
- ☐ Words of Knowledge
- ☐ Acts of Kindness
- ☐ Gospel

One last thing: Within the Weekly Five, I've spiced things up with an optional *challenge of the day.* This is designed to push those who want more of a challenge and create momentum for those who might have a hard time getting started with the Weekly Five.

A FEW MORE THINGS TO CONSIDER

Before you engage in the daily and weekly activations, I would like you to keep these things in mind:

- **The Holy Spirit is the greatest evangelist.** For the upcoming weeks, I would like you to remember to 1) keep evangelism authentic to who you are, 2) don't pressure yourself to do evangelism the same way you see others do it, and 3) celebrate where you're at, knowing that what you have right now is enough for God to transform someone's life!

- **Posture your heart in love and honor.** As you go out to minister this month, keep your love for people the highest priority! After years of training students, I have seen people get so excited to "do ministry" that they forget to love first. Remember, people are people, not projects.

- **Develop relationships.** We all love when salvation happens in a moment but sometimes it takes time to cultivate. Sometimes it can look like sowing seeds of the Gospel, listening, making yourself available and displaying genuine care and kindness. In the upcoming weeks, I encourage you to minister to people in this way. I assure you that as you do, the seeds you sow will grow!

- **Build rapport.** Rapport is a key ingredient of being relevant and not being awkward. It's like an icebreaker that builds instant connection with someone and lets people know you see them and value them. A great example of this is complimenting someone on their outfit or connecting about a current event or hobby. Another great way to build rapport is to ask people questions and learn from them. You can say, "How did you learn to play that instrument so well?" or, "How did you learn to shoot that basketball?" What you say doesn't necessarily have to be profound. Start with simple, authentic comments this month and see what God can do with it.

- **Be consistent.** Remember, the goal of the activations is for you to create a *lifestyle* of partnering with the Holy Spirit to touch the world around you. To do this, consistency is key. This month, you will be developing your voice to share the Gospel and spiritual muscles to step out and take risks. That being said, I encourage you to engage in these activations every day. But don't pressure yourself to be perfect. If you miss a day or if the activations don't go as planned, don't condemn yourself. There's grace! Just stay in a place of His presence, worship often to make sure your cup is overflowing, and act upon the Spirit's leading, and you will be well on your way to creating a lifestyle.

- **Make disciples.** After you lead someone to Jesus, you may feel the grace to take them under your wing and disciple them. Other times, you may not due to certain circumstances (you don't feel safe, gender, etc.) or distance (you lead someone to Jesus in a different town or online). Whether you disciple them or not, I encourage you to connect new believers to a local church. Also, if time permits and they are ready, I encourage you to baptize them both in water and in the Spirit. If you need guidance on how to do this, refer to page 101.

- **Have fun.** Remember that seriousness is not a fruit of the Spirit! We are called to walk in love, joy, and peace! In the weeks to come, I encourage you not to make these activations a rigid program, but rather an engaging adventure in which you get to partner with the Holy Spirit! So have fun, take risks, and know that the Spirit of the Lord is upon you!

/////////////

FAMILY

WEEK 1

It all began when one man, in one moment, with one word, shared the Gospel with me. That moment, as humble as it was, grew to eventually bring my mom, my dad, and my entire basketball team to salvation. Acts 1:8 says "But you will receive power when the Holy Spirit comes on you; and you will be my witnesses in Jerusalem, and in all Judea and Samaria, and to the ends of the earth" (NIV).

In this first week, I want you to focus on your family just as I did. I pray that as you do, you will see your compassion grow to transform your community and your world. *Your moment is now!*

COMPASSION DAY

A key to revival in your family is to develop compassion for them; to see them how He sees them; to love them how He loves them! Compassion is the full expression of God's passion towards us; it's the furious love in His heart expressed to us.

Picture yourself on trial in a courtroom. You have been found guilty of sin. But then Jesus, the Advocate, walks in and begins pleading mercy and grace on your behalf. Before the Judge whips down His gavel to sentence you to death, Jesus, moved by compassion, steps in and says He'll take your punishment upon Himself. Now picture Jesus, an innocent man, redeeming you as He takes your punishment by being nailed to a cross. That's compassion.

I want you to take a minute right now to pick one family member. In a moment, we will be asking the Lord to fill you with compassion for them.

Now, if you have been hurt by this family member, I want you to give the pain you've experienced to the Lord and forgive them. Give it to the Lord and say: "God, as You have forgiven me, give me the grace to forgive them." Now say it again. If you don't feel any different, that's okay. I believe God is doing a new thing in your heart.

Now, if you can, take this book and get into a quiet place. I encourage you to sit or lie down. Get comfortable. Once you're there:

- Ask the Father to show you the family member you chose. Ask Him to give you eyes to see how He sees your family member and the heart to love them the way He does. Say, "God, open my eyes to see _____ as You see him/her and fill my heart with compassion to love how You love him/her. Show me the thoughts that You have toward him/her because I know that Your thoughts are good."

- Imagine your family member saved, set free, and having a great relationship with you.

- Let thankfulness spring up in your heart for your family member—who God created him/her to be, including their gifting, calling, and identity in Jesus.

- Let that image settle, then get into a time of worship. Write down what the Holy Spirit tells/shows you:

_____

_____

_____

_____

_____

_____

_____

_____

_____

_____

_____

_____

_____

_____

_____

_____

_____

_____

_____

_____

_____

WEEKLY FIVE

As I stated earlier, the Weekly Five is the second lane that will cultivate an empowered lifestyle in you. It includes **prophecy, healing, words of knowledge, acts of kindness,** and **the Gospel**. I challenge you to find someone you can share these gifts with as you go about your week. Again, the goal is to check off all five of these activations by Day Seven. On Days Three and Seven, we will have a debrief session with you to check your progress and to encourage you.

A sample of what the Weekly Five check-in looks like is at the top of the next page.

5 WEEKLY FIVE

Check off the activations that you have completed this week.

- ☐ Prophetic
- ☐ Healing
- ☐ Words of Knowledge
- ☐ Acts of Kindness
- ☐ Gospel

Now, ask the Holy Spirit for eyes to see the ones around you who may need healing, a prophetic word, an act of kindness, a word of knowledge, and the Gospel shared with them. He may highlight someone you can share the Gospel with today as you're driving to work, or He might give you a word of knowledge for a coworker on Thursday. Just lean in and continue to talk with Him throughout the week.

I declare over you that as you step out and take risks, you will feel the Father's pleasure wash over you!

📅 CHALLENGE OF THE DAY

Tell the first stranger you see that Jesus loves them. Proceed to tell them anything else the Holy Spirit shows/tells you.

NOTES & REFLECTION

WORD DAY

There is power in the Word of God. Hebrews 4:12 says, "For the word of God is living and active and sharper than any two-edged sword..." (NASB). Praying and declaring the Word of God sets His promises in motion and places a target on our family members for the Lord to encounter them.

If Day One was about getting the right heart for your family member, Day Two is about meditating on a scripture that will encourage them. You are taking this scripture and applying it in two ways. The first way is praying and declaring the Word over them. For example, if God gives you Psalm 1:2-4, open it up and pray it over your family member. The second way is asking God how you can share that same scripture with them. This will be a powerful springboard for Day Five when you'll be connecting with them.

Right now, ask God for a scripture for your family member. Take this verse and begin interceding for them. If you need some help getting started, Psalm 103:2-5 is a great place to get God's heart for them. It says:

> *Bless the Lord, O my soul*
> *and forget not all his benefits,*
> *who forgives all your iniquity*
> *who heals all your diseases,*
> *who redeems your life from the pit,*
> *who crowns you with steadfast love and mercy,*
> *who satisfies you with good*
> *so that your youth is renewed like the eagle's (ESV).*

Now try praying it over your family member by plugging their name into the passage. It may look something like this:

> *Jesus, I ask You to release the benefits of Your King-*
> *dom on _____ today. Thank You for forgiving all*
> *of _____'s sins, mistakes and faults. Jesus, would*
> *You heal all of _____'s diseases today. Redeem*
> *_____'s life. Pour Your love and mercy upon him/*
> *her today. Fill _____ with Your goodness and*
> *restore him/her to Your original design.*

I want to encourage you not to overlook this section. Pray this a few times until you start to feel and believe that Jesus will really do what you're asking. Let your heart sink deep into a place of faith and intercession. I'm believing that as you pray, you will be stirred with the same faith as the Roman centurion who believed Jesus could heal his servant, even though he was not present (Matt. 8:5–13 NIV).

Now, give your family member a call or shoot them a text to see if they can meet with you this week. We have laid out a preferred time to connect with your family on Day Five (Encounter Day), but if they can't meet then, that's okay. Just try to give yourself enough cushion to complete Days Three (Gifts Day) and Four (Gospel Day).

There is flexibility and freedom in this schedule. The goal is for you to make an authentic connection with the person you're praying for. The best way to do this is to give them a heads up early in the week.

📅 CHALLENGE OF THE DAY

Go to your local gym or park, and ask the Lord to show you who needs a prophetic word.

_____
_____
_____
_____
_____
_____
_____
_____
_____
_____
_____
_____
_____
_____

CULTIVATING THE CRAFT

Giving Prophetic Words and Words of Knowledge

1 Corinthians 14:1 says, "Pursue love, yet desire earnestly spiritual *gifts...*" (NASB). Just as the Corinthian church was encouraged to prophesy and give words of knowledge (among other things), we too are to desire these gifts! Over the years I have seen the power of the prophetic and words of knowledge break self-hatred, prevent adultery, unlock God's worth and value in young men and women, reconcile sons back to fathers, and bring people into encounters with the love of Jesus. I want you to know that when you speak, you have access to the same possibilities ... and more! Your words are powerful!

WORDS OF KNOWLEDGE

There may be times when you're out and the Lord speaks to you about someone's past or present. Perhaps the Lord tells you that a young woman is dealing with back pain from an auto accident, or He speaks to you about releasing joy to a man who's going through depression. I want to encourage you this month to begin stepping out to inquire about these things. I believe God will use your interactions as stepping stones to reveal Himself.

Now here are some simple examples of *words of knowledge* as well as some corresponding questions:

- "Are you an author? I see you writing books."

- "I feel God showed me you're a phenomenal mom. Do you have children?"

- "I feel like God gave me a vision of you playing basketball with kids. Do you coach?"

- "When I walked past you, I got the sense that you have pain in your shoulder. Does your shoulder hurt?"

PROPHECY

Prophetic words can open a person's heart to experience God and/or bring confirmation to what He's already spoken to them. As you go, just keep in mind that prophecy consists of words that encourage, edify, and comfort.

Here are some examples of *simple prophetic* words:

- "I want you to know that God has a great plan and purpose for you."

- "You are so valuable."

- "I feel the Lord wants to fill you with His hope and joy."

- "Jesus loves you."

On the following page are a few examples of more *detailed prophetic* words.

- "The Lord showed me a picture of you being a missionary and preaching the Gospel all over the world."

- "I see you as a powerful business leader. I feel like you are going to create a business that blesses many families and changes the world."

- "I see you like a David in the Bible, a worshipper after God's own heart. I feel like your passion for the Lord is going to cause giants of torment to fall in people's lives."

- "Do you have a passion to open a restaurant? I see God opening doors for you to do that."

- "Do you have a passion to write? Because I feel like you're going to be writing a book soon."

If you get words that are negative or judgmental, I encourage you to pray into those words and ask the Lord for a solution to give. I once saw a man in Reno and had an impression he wasn't treating women right. I asked the Lord for a solution, then went up to him and shared with him that the Lord had called Him to be a protector of women. I could tell he was moved by the words and that they resonated with his heart, which gave me the opportunity to pray for him. I was later told that this man was a pimp!

NOTES & REFLECTION

GIFTS DAY

Day Three is setting the table for what Jesus did in John 4, when one word in one moment by one person so impacted a Samaritan woman's life that she led her entire town to Jesus. It's about you receiving the power of the Holy Spirit to rewrite your family's story.

Right now, I would like you to get into a peaceful place, turn on some worship music, and ask the Lord for a word that brings freedom, a word of knowledge that releases healing, or a prophetic word that propels your family member into his or her future.

1 Corinthians 14 says to pursue love and to desire spiritual gifts. Today, I declare a fresh hunger for the Spirit Himself, the Holy Spirit, because He's the reality of Heaven invading your family's life and is your source for hearing their needs. 1 Corinthians 12:7 says, "But the manifestation of the Spirit is given to each one for the profit *of all...*" (NKJV).

As you are listening to God for your family's needs, I encourage you to lean in to hear specific phrases and/or look for pictures that could really encourage your family.

Celebrate the smallest impressions the Lord shows you! Remember, you are now in the school of the Holy Spirit and you are learning His language. Whatever revelation you receive, ask the Lord to expand it; ask Him to show you more. For example, if you hear God say your family member has back pain, ask Him for specific details. Is it upper or lower back pain? What caused the back pain? Was it a car wreck, fall, or bike accident? Then ask the Lord how long that person has been dealing with it. Ask Him how they can be made whole from this incident.

Now ask Him similar questions about their emotional and spiritual well-being. Write down what you hear below. If you don't hear anything, it's OK. Sometimes God speaks in a still, small voice, so we may just need a little more time to lean in.

_____

_____

_____

_____

_____

_____

_____

_____

_____

_____

_____

_____

_____

_____

_____

5 **WEEKLY FIVE: MID-WEEK CHECK-IN**

Check off the activations that you have completed this week.

- ☐ Prophetic
- ☐ Healing
- ☐ Words of Knowledge
- ☐ Acts of Kindness
- ☐ Gospel

Take a moment right now to reflect upon Days One and Two. Did you engage with anyone? If so, what happened?

_____

_____

_____

_____

_____

_____

_____

_____

_____

_____

_____

_____

_____

_____

_____

_____

Write down any breakthroughs you received.

_____

_____

_____

_____

_____

_____

_____

_____

_____

_____

Ask the Holy Spirit to show you where He spoke to you this week. In what ways did He speak to you (dreams, nudges, impressions) that you weren't aware of?

_____

_____

_____

_____

_____

_____

_____

_____

_____

_____

_____

_____

Regardless of whether you responded to all the impressions the Holy Spirit gave you, I want you to know that He is pleased with you simply because you have said yes to the call! Success in the Kingdom is not the same as success in the world. While the world looks at what you have accomplished, the Father looks at the heart. He's looking at yours now and is pleased!

MIDWEEK DECLARATIONS

Before you leave today, say these out loud with me:

- I am great at sharing God's love!
- I hear God's voice well.
- I am a soul winner!
- The Holy Spirit makes evangelism easy!
- I am a walking divine encounter!
- The joy of the Lord is my strength.
- I am anointed to preach the Gospel!
- When I pray, the sick are made whole!
- The love of God will encounter my family.
- My children's children will experience the love and power of Jesus!

📅 CHALLENGE OF THE DAY

On your morning commute, buy a coffee and find someone you can give it to. Ask the Lord for an encouraging word you can give to them.

GOSPEL DAY

Jesus entrusted us with the privilege of taking the Gospel to the world around us. He could have chosen a variety of ways to draw men and women back to Him, but He chose you and me! This means He knows you have what it takes to carry the most important message to the world, and even more importantly, to your family.

Whether you're a seasoned evangelist or this is your first time sharing the Gospel, I want you to know there is no greater joy than seeing your family members encounter the love of God. I know this firsthand.

Before you set out to share the good news, I want to give you a good foundation for how to communicate it.

CULTIVATING THE CRAFT

How to Share the Gospel

I have learned four fundamental keys that make sharing the Gospel simple—God formed us, sin deformed us, Christ transforms us, repent and believe.

1. **God formed us.** A great place to start sharing the good news is establishing the reality of a person's value in Jesus, to value the way God created them. Here are a couple of scriptures you can use to share this thought:

    - Genesis 1:27–31: "God created man in His own image, in the image of God He created him; male and female He created them ... God saw all that He had made, and behold, it was very good" (NASB). When we tell people that God formed us, we are communicating that we are created in the image of God and that we are inherently very good.

    - Psalm 139:13–14: "For You formed my inward parts; You wove me in my mother's womb. I will give thanks to You, for I am fearfully and wonderfully made; Wonderful are Your works, And my soul knows it very well" (NASB). When we communicate that God formed us, we are telling people that they are not a mistake; that they are formed and fashioned in the likeness of God.

2. **Sin deformed us.** This is where we get to relate with people in their brokenness and communicate what opened the door to having a sin nature.

- Genesis 3:6: "So when the woman saw that the tree was good for food, and that it was a delight to the eyes, and that the tree was to be desired to make one wise, she took of its fruit and ate, and she also gave some to her husband who was with her, and he ate" (ESV). After we explain how we were made in God's image, it's good to talk about what separated mankind from Him: sin. For Adam and Eve, sin was rooted in fear, selfishness, and pride. Since then, we have all been affected by it.

- Galatians 5:19–21: "Now the works of the flesh are evident: sexual immorality, impurity, sensuality, idolatry, sorcery, enmity, strife, jealousy, fits of anger, rivalries, dissensions, divisions, envy, drunkenness, orgies, and things like these. I warn you, as I warned you before, that those who do such things will not inherit the kingdom of God" (ESV). This verse lays out a picture of what we were infected with and what keeps us from entering Heaven. When we talk about sin, it is vital that people understand what it is and how it separates them from God. After all, sin is what Jesus paid for.

3. **Christ transforms us.** This is my favorite part of the good news because it's where we get to share the transforming power of Jesus, where we proclaim that Jesus is the One who saves, heals, and delivers us!

- **2 Corinthians 5:17:** "Therefore if anyone is in Christ, he is a new creature; the old things passed away; behold, new things have come" (NASB). When we talk about transformation, we get to share how Christ broke the curse of sin, sickness, and death, and made us new creations in Him. This is the good news! We no longer have to live in fear and torment, but we get to live in righteousness, peace, and joy in the Holy Spirit!

- **Romans 6:4:** "Therefore we have been buried with Him through baptism into death, so that as Christ was raised from the dead through the glory of the Father, so we too might walk in newness of life" (NASB). Just as Jesus died and rose again, we, through baptism, go from being dead to coming alive in Him. This is the Gospel! Jesus brings the dead to life. He brings hope to the hopeless, freedom to the captives and peace to the tormented!

4. **Repent and Believe.** Once we've communicated the Gospel, we want to invite people to repent and believe. In case you are unfamiliar with what repentance is, it means to change one's mind, to turn around. Often, this looks like giving up control of doing life our own way and surrendering our lives to God. We acknowledge that we've missed the mark (that we've sinned) and we turn to the Person of Jesus.

- Romans 10:9–10: "If you declare with your mouth, "Jesus is Lord," and believe in your heart that God raised him from the dead, you will be saved. For it is with your heart that you believe and are justified, and it is with your mouth that you profess your faith and are saved" (NIV). When we give the invitation for someone to receive Christ, repentance is key! Often, when I lead someone to Jesus, I have them surrender every area of their life and say, "Jesus, You are the Lord of my life, and I will follow you."

The Gospel is really this simple. If you remember that *God formed us, sin deformed us, Christ transforms us, repent and believe,* you can powerfully share the Gospel in a variety of ways.

Now, I would like you to ask the Holy Spirit *how* you can share the Gospel with your family member. Ask Him, "How do I articulate the good news? How can I use *God formed us, sin deformed us, Christ transforms us, repent and believe?"* You may hear Him tell you to share it through your testimony or through a brief message, both of which I discuss on page 138.

I encourage you to do whatever He tells you. And in case you're thinking it's hard to share the Gospel, remember that it's as simple as God formed us, sin deformed us, Christ transforms us, repent and believe!

On the next page, write what Holy Spirit gives you.

_____
_____
_____
_____
_____
_____
_____
_____
_____

I understand it can be challenging to share the Gospel with your family, but I want to encourage you that you have what it takes to share the good news! Oftentimes, especially when we feel pressure, we have a tendency to think of how everything could go wrong, but right now, I want you to meditate on all the things that can go right by you taking a risk and sharing the Gospel.

Remember, it's the Holy Spirit who empowers us to be witnesses. When you connect with your family tomorrow, I encourage you to trust His leading, have fun, and go for it!

CHALLENGE OF THE DAY

Share your testimony with a complete stranger today and see if you can use it as an on ramp to share the Gospel. This may help you articulate the good news with your family member tomorrow.

NOTES & REFLECTION

ENCOUNTER DAY

This is the day! You have spent the last four days seeking the Lord, getting His heart and mind for your family member, and now you get to step out of the boat to share with them.

Right now, I want to stir up faith in your heart. Go ahead and declare this with me:

- God is restoring all things in my family and making them new!

- My faith is setting God's love in motion to encounter my family.

- His love and peace guide me. There is no pressure to perform.

- There are more for me than against me. Angels are by my side!

- _____'s heart is open and ready to receive the good news.

- God, Your heart is that _____ should not perish but have eternal life.

- Today is the day of salvation, healing and deliverance!

- God, You have given me the ministry of reconciliation. Today, I am Your ambassador. You have fully equipped me to be hope, light, and compassion to my family.

Let His love guide you through this day! See it from Heaven's perspective and know that you have nothing to lose and everything to gain!

READY, RELEVANT, AND REVELATORY

Right now, I want to introduce to you the Three Rs: *ready, relevant,* and *revelatory.* The Three Rs are the basics of communication so that we're prepared and not overly awkward when we share the love of Jesus. For the next few weeks we'll be covering these three words, but right now I want to focus briefly on **Ready.**

2 Timothy 4:2-5 says, "Preach the word; be ready in season *and* out of season ... be sober in all things, endure hardship, do the work of an evangelist, fulfill your ministry" (NASB). To be ready in season and out of season, you need to practice.

When many read about David and Goliath, they focus on the end of the story, when David kills Goliath. As a result, they see the victory. What they don't see, however, is the preparation. Before David killed Goliath, he spent time in the wilderness building the confidence to wield his sling. We know this because in 1 Samuel 17:36, he tells Saul, the king of Israel, "Your servant has killed both the lion and the bear; and this uncircumcised Philistine will be like one of them, since he has taunted the armies of the living God"

(NASB). In the end, David's private victory became a breakthrough for the whole nation.

Just as David was prepared to throw stones at Goliath, I believe that your preparation through the last four days has readied you to defeat the giants oppressing your family. I want to encourage you now to say that *you* have the stones.

Take ten minutes now to gather everything the Lord has spoken to you over the past four days—your compassion, your scriptures, your prophetic revelations, and your key Gospel message—and thank Him for the big and small revelations He has shown you.

Now ask the Lord to stir your heart and to give you peace, joy and confidence.

Before you reach out to your family member, take ten minutes to worship and pray. I want you to again envision your family member healed, set free, and loving Jesus. Prophetically declare, "Thank You for making _____ whole and free. Thank You for filling _____ with Your peace and that You're the One who makes impossible things possible."

📅 CHALLENGE OF THE DAY

Walk or jog around your neighborhood and find one person to whom you can give a word of knowledge.

INTERCESSION DAY

Day Six is a day of worship and prayer. Yesterday, you took a risk and connected with your family member. We pray that no matter how it turned out, you feel the Lord's pleasure over you. You did so well to obey His leading, and I believe that what you've sown will bear fruit. Speaking of fruit, no plant ever grows without first watering the seed. This is the heart behind Day Six.

Powerful and effective prayer invites breakthrough. James 5:16–18 says, "The effective prayer of a righteous man can accomplish much. Elijah was a man with a nature like ours, and he prayed earnestly that it would not rain, and it did not rain on the earth for three years and six months. Then he prayed again, and the sky poured rain and the earth produced its fruit" (NASB).

Notice here that it was through Elijah's prayers that the rain came to produce fruit. In like fashion, when we pray for others, God will water the seeds we have sown and they will bear fruit. I experienced this firsthand with the salvation of my family and college basketball team and even now, with the significant transformation of our city of

Redding, California. When I press in and pray, breakthrough comes, power is released, and people get saved. I declare that as you pray for your family member today, you will experience the same fruit.

Right now, I'd like you to pray for your family member in the secret place, keeping in mind that prayer is the fertilizer for the seeds you planted and that angels are released on your behalf. Take 10–15 minutes to thank God for the encounter He has for that family member. Release peace and cover him or her. Pray that the seeds that were planted would grow, that your family member's heart toward God would continue to open, that a real relationship would blossom from your encounter yesterday, and that God would give you a key to their heart on your follow-up with them tomorrow.

Write anything He shows you:

_____

_____

_____

_____

_____

_____

_____

_____

_____

_____

_____

_____

_____

_____

_____

_____

_____

_____

_____

_____

_____

_____

_____

_____

_____

_____

_____

_____

_____

_____

_____

_____

_____

_____

_____

_____

★ CHALLENGE OF THE DAY

Find a local business that has really blessed you and give the owner/
manager an encouraging word via letter, phone call, or in person.

FOLLOW-UP DAY

This day is about discipleship. Discipleship focuses on consistently making yourself available to unsaved people so that they don't have to run the race of life alone. This is the heart behind Day Seven—consistency. When people walk with you and see how you interact with others, handle problems, treat your kids, and trust the Lord, it makes an impact. When they walk with you, they learn to trust you and become awakened to His love.

Today, I want you to follow up with your family member. This can range from sending a text, saying, "Hey, I'm so excited that we got to connect. Thanks for making time for me" to you having a Bible study with them in your living room—whatever you feel there's grace for. Keep these recommendations in mind:

- Be consistent.
- Make yourself available. Consider joining them in one of their passions.
- Be slow to speak and quick to listen.
- Be intentional.

- While you're with them, pray for guidance and trust the leading of the Holy Spirit.

In John 4:34, Jesus says, "My food is to do the will of Him who sent Me and to finish His work" (NKJV). I would like to propose that God's work is what nourishes us, too.

As you pour into your family today, know that you're helping to finish the work of the Father. Also, know that it is the key to the harvest manifesting in your personal life. You are the light of the world, a child of God, an ambassador of the King. Be bold, carry His love, and have fun.

Tip: After you follow up with your family member, I recommend completing the Week One Encouragement and Reflection section located on the following page instead of saving it for tomorrow. This will help you keep a good rhythm for the week.

CHALLENGE OF THE DAY

Scroll through your friends on social media until you find someone God highlights. Ask Him what encouraging word you can give that person, then send a private message.

NOTES & REFLECTION

ENCOURAGEMENT & REFLECTION

I want you to know that God is pleased and proud of you for saying yes to Him, for letting the Holy Spirit empower your life, and taking the risk to step out of the boat.

Whatever the outcome was this week—whether you saw a family member saved or you experienced nothing but rejection—don't get hung up on the fruit but know that the Father is celebrating you and your obedience, for you have opened the door for the King and His Kingdom to come.

Now, I would like you to take a few moments to answer these questions:

What surprised you this week? Did you find the activation to be easier than expected? Write down why.

_____

_____

_____

_____

How did you grow this week?

_____

_____

_____

_____

_____

_____

What obstacles did you encounter this week? How do you plan to overcome them?

_____

_____

_____

_____

_____

_____

If your family member wasn't saved, healed, or delivered, take five minutes to ask the Holy Spirit, "Are there any keys that I could have released to see him/her saved, healed, or delivered?" Write His answers here:

_____

_____

_____

_____

_____

_____

_____

5 WEEKLY FIVE

Check off the activations that you have completed this week.

- ☐ Prophetic
- ☐ Healing
- ☐ Words of Knowledge
- ☐ Acts of Kindness
- ☐ Gospel

Take a moment right now to reflect upon the week. What was your high point and low point?

_____

_____

_____

_____

Write down your favorite testimony in a brief and powerful way:

_____

_____

_____

_____

Congratulations. You've finished the first week! God is crafting something beautiful in you. Philippians 1:6 says, "Being confident of this, that he who began a good work in you will carry it on to completion until the day of Christ Jesus" (NIV). Well done!

NOTES & REFLECTION

COWORKERS & FRIENDS

WEEK 2

This week we're going to take our focus to another level and let the ripple effects of your life touch your coworkers and friends. This is the next wave that our lives naturally influence. This is the ripple effect that extends from our families so that we can eventually impact the world.

Every believer is called to fulfill the Great Commission; I believe that starts with the people closest to us. In this section, I want to help you create a mindset of seeing your workplace and friendships as the mission field the Lord has called you to.

COMPASSION DAY

Matthew 9:36 says that Jesus "...was moved with compassion..." (NKJV). This often came when He was out doing life, when those who were hungry, hurting, and distressed came to Him.

I believe compassion is often birthed in us this way, too. When we see a need in someone else's life, like a homeless mom on the street with her children, our hearts are moved and we are compelled to act. In a similar way, when we see those who don't know Jesus walking on a path that leads to Hell, we should lean into His heart of compassion that says, "Come to me, all you who are weary and burdened, and I will give you rest. Take my yoke upon you and learn from me, for I am gentle and humble in heart, and you will find rest for your souls. For my yoke is easy and my burden is light" (Matt. 11:28-30, NASB).

I want you to take a couple of minutes to think about a profound moment when Jesus had compassion on you—when you were burdened and He took your weight upon Himself; when you were distressed and He took a moment to be with you and bring you peace. This is the same compassion Jesus has charged us to carry to the world.

Today, we're going to stir up compassion differently. Instead of abiding in a private place, like you did last week, I would like you to walk through your workplace and let your heart feel what Jesus feels for others. Do the same thing when you're around your friends. Realize that no matter how accomplished or broken an individual seems, people are people and we have an assignment to bring the Kingdom to them.

As you're out at work or among friends this week:

- Pick one person to focus on and begin a dialogue with the Father about him or her. Let His compassion for that person well up in you.

- Imagine that individual encountering the Father. Picture him or her being filled with His love, peace, and freedom.

- Make a point of connection. Compliment that person, encourage him or her, and ask if you can connect with him or her later in the week.

- Remember that your presence and words are powerful.

WEEKLY FIVE

Many of you are building muscles that may never have been developed. I want to tell you *great job, keep going,* and *remain diligent.* Anything worthwhile takes time and discipline to develop.

74

As you remain consistent in taking risks, you will, like a seasoned musician, become skilled in the craft of soul winning.

Again, the goal of the Weekly Five is to check off all five of these activations—**healing, prophecy, acts of kindness, words of knowledge** and **the Gospel**—by Day Seven. On Day Three and Seven, we will have a debrief session with you to check your progress and to encourage you.

5 WEEKLY FIVE

Check off the activations that you have completed this week.

☐ Prophetic
☐ Healing
☐ Words of Knowledge
☐ Acts of Kindness
☐ Gospel

Right now, ask the Holy Spirit for eyes to see the ones around you who may need healing, a prophetic word, an act of kindness, a word of knowledge, or the Gospel shared with them. He may give you a word of encouragement to share with your barista or He might stir you to share your testimony with your grocery clerk. Just lean in and continue to talk with the Holy Spirit throughout the week.

I declare over you that this is going to be a week of breakthrough in the gifts of the Spirit. Remember the same Spirit that raised Christ from the dead lives in you!

 CHALLENGE OF THE DAY

Text a coworker or friend and ask if you can bring them a coffee. As you buy it, ask the Holy Spirit for an encouraging word you can give and then deliver it.

_____

_____

_____

_____

_____

_____

_____

_____

_____

_____

_____

_____

_____

_____

_____

_____

_____

_____

NOTES & REFLECTION

WEEK 2: DAY 2

WORD DAY

The Bible says that the right word in the right season is like gold apples in settings of silver (Prov. 25:11). The right word from the Lord in the right season can awaken somebody to the reality that the Lord is real and knows them.

Yesterday you went out and sought God's heart for your coworker or friend, and today you are seeking a word that will be like that gold apple for them, a word that I believe will stir a hunger for more of the Lord.

Right now, take 10–15 minutes to:

- Open your Bible and begin praying for your coworker or friend. Ask the Lord to give you a specific passage for that person and ask Him what it means. For example, if He highlights Proverbs 3:5, which states, "Trust in the Lord with all your heart and do not lean on your own understanding" (ESV), He may be telling you that your coworker/friend feels as if they don't have direction in life.

This would be your opportunity to encourage that person to trust in God with all their heart.

- Ask the Lord how you can share this scripture with them creatively. For example, you may feel led to text or call your coworker/friend to let them know you're praying for them and have a scripture to encourage them. Or you may feel led to give them the prophetic word in a card, enclosed with a gift certificate.

When you release the Word of God with a loving heart, it will be like living water to someone's soul. As you declare the Word of God over your coworker/friend this week, I pray that it releases hope, peace, and joy!

📅 CHALLENGE OF THE DAY

As you're going about your day, look for one person who is ill or disabled. Take a moment to pray for them in person.

CULTIVATING THE CRAFT

Giving Scripture-Based Prophetic Words

Here are a few considerations for giving a prophetic word:

- Does your word encourage and give life?
- Is it comforting?
- Is it edifying? Test it on yourself first.

As you begin to create a prophetic culture in your life, know that your prophetic words:

1. Should express the heart of the Father to people, which is the promise of "life and life abundantly" (John 10:10).

2. Should be told through the lens of the finished work of the cross.

3. Should communicate to people that God isn't *mad at* them but *madly in love* with them!

Here are some examples of what scripture-based prophetic words *might look like:*

- God is giving you a hope and future (Jer. 29:11).
- Jesus loves you and you can trust Him (John. 3:16, Prov. 3:5–6).
- I see God filling you with peace and hope (Rom. 5:1–5).

John 10:10 says, "The thief comes only to steal and kill and destroy" (NIV). When you share a prophetic word, make sure that your words don't devalue, diminish, or destroy. That's what the devil does and trust me, he doesn't need any help.

Here are what scripture-based prophetic words *shouldn't* look like:

- "There is a dark cloud over your life. I see you falling into a drug addiction."
- "The devil is after you and your family. You better watch your back."
- "I see you getting sick, losing your job, and getting into a car wreck, but don't worry. After this trial is over, God is going to bless you."

If you feel or see something negative after asking the Holy Spirit for a word, I recommend asking Him for a solution to what He has shown you. Take, for instance, the second example in the previous list: "The devil is after you and your family." It may be possible that this revelation you received is good information. If you feel that you should share what you have, I again suggest that you state the solution. You could say something along the lines of, "I feel that Jesus wants to protect you and your family. Psalm 91:4 says, 'He will cover you with his feathers, and under his wings you will find refuge'" (NIV).

NOTES & REFLECTION

GIFTS DAY

Debate is always at the mercy of experience! Again, Paul said, "I did not come to you in the wisdom of man, but in a demonstration of Spirit and power." As you focus on your coworker or friend today, ask Jesus for a fresh outpouring of His power!

Right now, I want to stir up the prophetic in you. So go ahead and stand up, walk around, and take five minutes to pray in the Spirit. As you are doing this, think about your coworker/friend. Remember that praying in the Spirit strengthens and edifies your spirit; it calibrates you to God's heart and what He is doing. Many times as I pray in the Spirit, the Lord will guide me with clear impressions and directions to pray.

Write down what you hear:

_____

_____

_____

_____

_____

Now I want you to focus on healing. I want you to visualize your coworker/friend touched by the power of God and made whole from sickness. Let this build faith in your heart and begin declaring Isaiah 53:5 over them, "But He was pierced for our transgressions; he was crushed for our iniquities; upon him was the chastisement that brought us peace, and with his wounds we are healed." (ESV).

Write down anything God shows you:

_____

_____

_____

_____

_____

_____

_____

_____

_____

_____

_____

_____

_____

Now that you're back, I want you to declare this: "Jesus, I thank You that by Your wounds _____ is healed. Jesus, I thank You that You have power over sickness, disease, and death. I declare Your power to touch _____ . God fill _____ with Your love. Show them how near You are and wash over them with Your peace."

5 WEEKLY FIVE: MID-WEEK CHECK-IN

Check off the activations that you have completed this week.

- ☐ Prophetic
- ☐ Healing
- ☐ Words of Knowledge
- ☐ Acts of Kindness
- ☐ Gospel

Take a moment right now to reflect upon Days One and Two. Did you engage with anyone? If so, what happened?

_____

_____

_____

_____

_____

_____

_____

_____

_____

_____

_____

_____

_____

_____

Write down any breakthroughs you received.

_____
_____
_____
_____
_____
_____
_____
_____
_____

Ask the Holy Spirit to show you where He spoke to you this week. In what ways did He speak to you (dreams, nudges, impressions) that you weren't aware of at the time?

_____
_____
_____
_____
_____
_____
_____
_____
_____
_____

You're doing a great job this week! Kris Vallotton says, "Before you do something extraordinary, you have to do the ordinary in an extraordinary way." I want to encourage you that you're doing just that. You're changing the world through His love, day by day, activation by activation!

CHALLENGE OF THE DAY

Look for windows to share two words of knowledge as you're going about your day.

NOTES & REFLECTION

_____

_____

_____

_____

_____

_____

_____

_____

_____

_____

_____

_____

_____

_____

_____

GOSPEL DAY

The greatest miracle is a life born again, a dead person coming alive. Over the last three days, we have been seeking the Lord for a coworker or friend. We have been preparing ourselves to share God's heart with them by stirring compassion, praying the Word of God, and asking the Lord to touch them with power.

In a moment, here is what I want you to do:

- Envision yourself sharing your testimony with your coworker/friend. Imagine it flowing from your heart clearly and powerfully.
- Now imagine that your coworker/friend becomes eager to know more, which opens an opportunity for you to share the Gospel.
- Envision yourself articulating the good news well. You tell them that Jesus died for us on a cross, defeated death, rose from the grave, and is now seated with the Father.
- Imagine yourself inviting your coworker/friend to receive Jesus. You tell them that Jesus is knocking on the door of

their heart and that there's an opportunity to receive the gift of salvation.

- As you look into your coworker or friend's face, imagine their eagerness to receive this gift.
- Now imagine leading them to the Lord as you're gripped with compassion. Witness their eyes opening for the first time as they come fully alive.
- Lastly, envision yourself baptizing them and declaring to your other coworkers and friends that this person has found a new hope in Jesus. See them becoming like the woman at the well, where they become a spokesperson for God's goodness.

Seeing is believing! If you can see it, it will build your faith for greater things. After all, faith is what moves mountains. Remember, Jesus has empowered you with the Holy Spirit! Trust Him in this time as you step out and take risks in the next couple of days.

Currently, I mobilize 2,500 students in Bethel School of Supernatural Ministry's outreach department. Every year, many of these students lead people to the Lord, even when they thought they couldn't. I want to encourage you now that if they can do it, you can too. The same Spirit who empowers them has empowered you to be a witness.

Sometime today, I would like you to share your testimony with a friend you're comfortable with and then get feedback. You can also role play with them if they already know your story. Doing this will sharpen you to articulate the Gospel well for your coworker/friend tomorrow.

CHALLENGE OF THE DAY

Share the Gospel with one of your Christian friends and ask
for feedback.

NOTES & REFLECTION

_____

_____

_____

_____

_____

_____

_____

_____

_____

_____

_____

_____

_____

_____

_____

_____

_____

_____

_____

_____

_____

ENCOUNTER DAY

Last week, we covered how to be ready in season and out of season, ready to preach, exhort, and encourage the people around you. This week, I want to talk to you about being relevant—what it looks like to connect with the people around you.

Whether it's your nephew who loves basketball or your neighbor who loves surfing, you want to be looking for ways to connect with people in meaningful and relevant ways. Keeping this in mind will be especially helpful as you connect with your coworker or friend today.

My definition of *relevant* is speaking the culture's language. It's being current without compromise and transforming culture without conforming to it.

Here are a few ways you could do this today:

- Ask your coworker/friend what their favorite hobby is.
- Ask them about their passions and dreams for their future.
- Ask the story behind their tattoos.

- Ask them questions about their family. Try not to generalize your questions. Be intentional with what you ask. For example, if you know your coworker's wife sells makeup, you can ask him how her business is doing.
- Ask what they are doing this weekend.
- Connect on a current event (i.e. celebrity death, natural disasters, current movies).

Connecting on questions like these may seem like common sense, but some of us miss the opportunity to thread the Gospel into what matters to people.

Right now, I want to begin stirring up faith in your heart. Declare the following with me:

- I hear God's voice well. Thank You, God, for speaking through me.
- _____ is going to encounter the love of Jesus today.
- Today is the day of salvation, healing, and deliverance!
- His love and peace guide me. There is no pressure to perform.
- I have been commissioned to bring the Gospel to my coworkers and friends!

Take ten minutes now to gather everything the Lord has spoken to you over the past four days—your compassion, your scriptures, your prophetic revelations, and your key Gospel message. Take some time with them and thank the Lord for speaking to you. Then celebrate the big and small revelations He has shown you.

Remember that God is going to use everything you have sown in the secret place as you step out in faith today. Know that He is with you and is proud of you!

 CHALLENGE OF THE DAY

Make/get an extra lunch and take it to someone unexpected. Then ask the Holy Spirit if He has anything else to give them.

NOTES & REFLECTION

_____

_____

_____

_____

_____

_____

_____

_____

_____

_____

_____

_____

_____

_____

_____

_____

_____

INTERCESSION DAY

Today, I would like you to rejoice, reflect, and re-engage. Rejoice in God for what He's doing through you; reflect on how the encounter with your coworker or friend went; and re-engage in prayer for the Lord to water the seeds you planted yesterday.

God says He can move a mountain with even just a mustard seed of faith. As you pray with faith, I believe He is going to increase what He did yesterday. If your coworker/friend did not receive Jesus, He will remove the obstacles that are keeping that person from receiving Him. If they did receive Jesus, they will encounter Him in a personal and profound way that roots them deep in His love.

Now take 10 minutes to rejoice, reflect, and re-engage. As you do, write here what the Holy Spirit tells you:

_____

_____

_____

_____

_____

Believe that whatever you prayed will happen and be set into motion, that God will become real to your coworker/friend, and that they will know without a doubt that God encountered them.

Remember that God will water the seeds you have sown to bear fruit; that when you press in and pray, breakthrough comes, power is released, and people get saved. I declare that your prayers for your coworker/friend today will bear this kind of fruit.

Write anything He shows you for your point of connection tomorrow:

_____

_____

_____

_____

_____

_____

_____

_____

_____

_____

_____

_____

_____

_____

_____

_____

_____

_____

_____

_____

CULTIVATING THE CRAFT
Water Baptism and the Baptism of the Holy Spirit

When the opportunity comes for you to lead someone to Jesus, I highly encourage you to pray for the person to be filled with the Spirit as well and that you find a place to baptize them. This releases the Holy Spirit's supernatural power in their lives and allows them to walk in the fullness of who the Father made them to be.

WATER BAPTISM

A water baptism is a public declaration to the world of what God is doing in one's heart. It identifies with the death and resurrection of Jesus and declares that as He died, so did we, and as He rose, so we also rose in new life! (Rom. 6:4).

What you should know about water baptism:

You don't need a license, nor do you need to be an ordained pastor to baptize someone. In the book of Acts, Jesus actually empowered *all* His disciples/believers to baptize. *All* includes you!

You can baptize just about anywhere (Acts 8:34–38). Some denominations believe that baptism must be done at church, but most bodies of water will suffice: pools, rivers, hot tubs, bathtubs, horse troughs, lakes, and oceans are all great options.

Pray and prophesy over the person either before or after they are baptized. In doing this myself, I have seen a lot of people get healed and delivered.

As you submerge the person in water, say, "I baptize you in the name of the Father, Son, and the Holy Spirit," just as Jesus commissioned us to do in Matthew 28:19.

SPIRIT BAPTISM

After water baptism, I encourage you to pray for the person to be filled with the Spirit! This is called the baptism of the Holy Spirit. It is the key to a believer living free and full of life. Before the disciples were filled with the Spirit, they scattered from Jesus, fearing that they might lose their lives. But after they were filled with the Spirit, they were bold and fierce, willing to lay their lives down for the Gospel. This is why we need the fire of the Holy Spirit in our lives. It's the Holy Spirit who emboldens us to take the Gospel to the ends of the earth!

My tips for baptizing someone in the Holy Spirit:

- Have the person fix their eyes on the Father and His presence. In Acts 2, when the Holy Spirit fell, we are told that the disciples were in one accord; that their hearts were aligned and connected to the Father. If the person is anxious, ask them to close their eyes and calm down. When people get anxious around me, I'll say something to the effect of, "The best way to accept a promise or gift is simply to receive it. Put your hands out and accept it. Don't strive, just receive."

- Pray simply. When you ask the Holy Spirit to fill the person, you don't need to be wordy or profound. I usually say simple things like, "Fill them, Holy Spirit, come Holy Spirit."

- Lead people into an awareness of what the Holy Spirit is doing. After praying, "Fill them, Holy Spirit, come Holy Spirit," ask the person, "What do you feel like the Holy Spirit is doing right now?"

  - If they feel His presence or they say, "I feel a pressure/ bubbling," or "I feel like a word is coming out," it's important to affirm what God's doing and encourage the person to release it.

  - If they tell you, "I don't feel anything at all," encourage them to ask for the gift of the Holy Spirit themselves. In Luke 11:13, Jesus says, "If you then, though you are evil, know how to give good gifts to your children, how much more will your Father in heaven give the Holy Spirit to those who ask him!" (NIV)

Water baptism and the baptism of the Holy Spirit are what empower every believer to live freely and powerfully! So the next time you lead someone to Jesus, make sure to ask if they have been baptized. Remember that you have been commissioned!

CHALLENGE OF THE DAY

Take a friend out for a drive around town until you feel led to stop somewhere. Together, give a prophetic word, pray for healing and/ or share the Gospel with someone. Who knows? Maybe you'll knock out your Weekly Five in one shot!

NOTES & REFLECTION

FOLLOW-UP DAY

Early in my Christian walk, I struggled with high school calculus. It didn't come naturally for me, so I decided to seek help from the after-school tutoring program. As I walked through the door, a woman directed me to a table where a small Hawaiian man named Lane took me under his wing. I remember feeling happy to have received help so quickly.

Lane was a kind, generous, and fun man. He would tutor me and a few others at his house and break calculus equations down into sports analogies. Eventually, during football season, he began inviting me over like I was family. I still recall Lane asking if I would like to watch the football game with his friends after we finished up with my lessons. This was especially impactful for me because I knew he was making a lot of space for me in his already-busy life.

On the day of my tests, Lane would meet me at the pancake house at 5 a.m. and give me a pre-test that he had written himself. I would take it while we ate breakfast and after I completed it, he would grade it and go over what I did wrong. He did this week after week, test after test, going above and beyond to show God's love for me and to encourage me in my faith. I can't tell you how important this was in my early years of following Jesus.

As you prepare to follow up with your coworker/friend today, you don't have to feel the pressure of doing as much as Lane did for me—but know that your ability to connect with the hearts of the people you disciple makes all the difference. Lane's continual sacrifice, love, and willingness to go the extra mile imprinted the relentless love of the Father on my life. I am confident that as you demonstrate this type of consistent love, others will be as impacted as I was. Don't ever underestimate the moments you create with people.

Before you pour into your coworker/friend today, I want to share with you a quote from my friend, Tom Crandall. He says, "Before you touch a thousand at one time, you need to touch one thousands of times." It's the small things done often that make big impacts—the intentional phone calls, your encouraging words on a birthday, buying coffee, etc. So remember to celebrate the small moments and know that your presence makes a difference.

📅 CHALLENGE OF THE DAY

Call someone who has made an impact on your life and encourage them. If they're saved, ask if they have a family member to whom you can give a prophetic word. If they're not, find an opening to share the Gospel.

Reminder: After you follow up with your coworker/friend, I recommend completing the Week Two Encouragement and Reflection section on the following pages instead of saving it for tomorrow. This will help you keep a good rhythm for the week.

NOTES & REFLECTION

_____

_____

_____

_____

_____

_____

_____

_____

_____

_____

_____

_____

_____

_____

_____

_____

_____

_____

_____

_____

_____

_____

_____

ENCOURAGEMENT & REFLECTION

As you can see, we are creating a rhythm for you to become effective at discipleship and soul winning. Like farmers who bring in the harvest during the right season or fishermen who catch fish at the right time of day, we too are creating rhythms to connect with the people around us.

This week you focused on your coworker/friend. You went on a journey with the Holy Spirit, stirring up compassion, praying key scriptures, activating the gifts of the Spirit, and communicating the Gospel in a relevant way with that person. You did all this to throw out your net in faith to impact those you interact with daily. This rhythm you are creating is establishing a lifestyle of intentionality, which in turn will generate mighty ripple effects that release the Kingdom to the world around you.

Whether you saw a mighty salvation, healing, or deliverance this week or you planted seeds of His love and kindness, be encouraged that when you abide in and love Him and others, you will eventually bear fruit. Continue to be faithful in the process, celebrate the small victories, and lean into the Holy Spirit if you're facing any roadblocks.

A few years ago, I led a high school outreach during lunchtime. My team and I couldn't seem to get the breakthrough we believed the Lord had for us but we made a decision to press in, joining together earlier on the campus to worship and pray with a teacher in the classroom. Our goal was simple: seek God, get encouraged in His presence, and ask for keys to see Jesus exalted on the campus. A few weeks into the prayer meetings, everything turned around: Doors that had not been opened burst wide and people who were not for us became some of our biggest supporters. Teachers began to see miracles with students and most of all, we saw an increase in salvations, healings, and deliverances during our lunchtime meetings. This is the power of perseverance and relying on the Holy Spirit when we need breakthrough! If you need a breakthrough at work or with your friend, continue to abide; I promise you that the Lord will demonstrate His power.

Now, take a few moments to answer these questions:

What surprised you this week? Did you find this activation to be more challenging than the previous week? Write down why.

_____

_____

_____

_____

_____

_____

_____

_____

In what way(s) did you grow this week?

_____

_____

_____

_____

_____

What obstacles did you encounter this week? How do you plan to overcome them?

_____

_____

_____

_____

_____

If your coworker or friend wasn't saved, healed, or delivered, take five minutes to ask the Holy Spirit, "Are there any keys that I could have released to see him/her saved, healed, or delivered?" Write His answers here:

_____

_____

_____

_____

_____

_____

5 **WEEKLY FIVE**

Check off the activations that you have completed this week.

- ☐ Prophetic
- ☐ Healing
- ☐ Words of Knowledge
- ☐ Acts of Kindness
- ☐ Gospel

Write down your favorite testimony in a brief and powerful way:

_____

_____

_____

_____

_____

_____

_____

_____

_____

_____

_____

_____

_____

_____

_____

_____

_____

Which Weekly Five activation have you grown in the most—healing, words of knowledge, the prophetic, acts of kindness, or sharing the Gospel? What do you believe was the key?

_____

_____

_____

_____

_____

_____

_____

_____

_____

_____

Romans 10:14–15 says, "But how can they call on him to save them unless they believe in him? And how can they believe in him if they have never heard about him? And how can they hear about him unless someone tells them? And how will anyone go and tell them without being sent? That is why the Scriptures say, "How beautiful are the feet of messengers who bring good news!" (NLT)

I want to remind you that you are the messenger; you are the one who has been sent! For the last two weeks, you've shown up and have spread the message of the Gospel. So whether you saw fruit this week or not, you need to know that Jesus calls your feet beautiful and that what you are doing moves His heart. What you're doing is bringing His children home!

NOTES & REFLECTION

_____
_____
_____
_____
_____
_____
_____
_____
_____
_____
_____
_____
_____
_____
_____
_____
_____
_____
_____
_____
_____
_____
_____
_____
_____
_____
_____
_____
_____
_____

//////////

NEIGHBORS

WEEK 3

In Week Three, we are going to take the momentum we've built reaching our families and coworkers and use it to touch our neighbors. I want to remind you of the powerful commission Jesus gives us in Acts 1:8: "But you will receive power when the Holy Spirit has come upon you; and you shall be My witnesses both in Jerusalem, and in all Judea and Samaria, and even to the remotest part of the earth" (NASB).

Just as Samaria was a neighbor to Judea, so are the people who live next to us. This week, as you cross paths with your neighbors, I want you to think about how Jesus stopped for the woman at the well in John 4. Again, it took one word in one moment from one man to transform her life! I want to encourage you that this week, you could do the same.

COMPASSION DAY

Creating an impactful relationship with our neighbors is not difficult, but it can easily be overlooked if we are not intentional about it. Remember that sometimes evangelism looks like doing the little things consistently.

Jesus said in Matthew 22:37, "'You shall love the Lord your God with all your heart, and with all your soul, and with all your mind.' This is the greatest and foremost commandment. The second is like it, 'You shall love your neighbor as yourself.'"

Loving the people who live around you is one of the commandments Jesus gave us. My question to you is: What does loving *your* neighbors look like? Today I want to take you on a journey of unlocking and activating compassion in your heart so that you, in turn, can touch the neighbors Jesus has placed around you.

Take 10–15 minutes to turn on some worship music and ask the Holy Spirit to show you practical ways you can love your neighbors. Write down what He shows you on the next page.

_____

_____

_____

_____

_____

_____

_____

_____

_____

In a moment, here is what I would like you to do:

- Take a few minutes to walk around your neighborhood and figure out which neighbors you know. If you don't know any neighbors, meet one. Then start praying that God would encounter that neighbor's home and their family.

- Ask the Lord to fill you with compassion for your neighbor. Then envision Him touching each one of their family members. Ask the Lord to show you who He created each one of them to be and their God-given talents and skills. Envision Him healing their bodies, filling them with joy, hope, and peace. Ask the Lord to send angels to their home at night to encounter them.

- Begin praying for them. It could look something like this: "God, I thank you for _____ . Give me compassion in my heart for_____ . Fill my heart with the same love You have for him/her. I bless _____ today. God, does _____ know You?

Show me how to love _____ this week. Show me how I can serve_____ and reveal Your goodness to him/her."

- Make a point of connection. Connecting with your neighbor could be as simple as knocking on their front door to introduce yourself. I would like you to take the time today to encourage them and ask if they could connect later in the week. This is your opportunity to establish or strengthen your relationship.

WEEKLY FIVE

Again, the goal of the Weekly Five is to check off all five of these activations—**healing, prophecy, acts of kindness, words of knowledge,** and **the Gospel**—by Day Seven. On Days Three and Seven, we will have a debrief session with you to check your progress and to encourage you.

5 WEEKLY FIVE

Check off the activations that you have completed this week.

- ☐ Prophetic
- ☐ Healing
- ☐ Words of Knowledge
- ☐ Acts of Kindness
- ☐ Gospel

Right now, ask the Holy Spirit for eyes to see the ones around you who may need healing, a prophetic word, an act of kindness, a word of knowledge, or the Gospel shared with them. He may stir you to pray for the sick person you see on your lunch break, or you might be moved to make extra meals for the people in need in your community. Just lean in and continue to talk with the Holy Spirit throughout the week.

Mark 16:20 says, "And they went out and preached everywhere, while the Lord worked with them, and confirmed the word by the signs that followed" (NASB). I declare over you that this week you will experience the same thing; that God will work with you and confirm the word by the signs that follow you!

📅 CHALLENGE OF THE DAY

Go to your local coffee or smoothie shop, buy a drink, and bless the workers with a generous tip and an encouraging word.

NOTES & REFLECTION

WORD DAY

Psalm 107:20 says, "He sent His word and healed them, and delivered them from their destructions" (NASB). Declaring the Word of God over your neighbors is a powerful weapon for breakthrough. It releases the promises of God to heal and deliver.

Right now, take 10–15 minutes to read Psalm 91. For every three to four verses of the passage, I would like you to pause, engage with what you've read, and then pray over your neighbor. Below is an example of what this might look like.

Psalm 91:1–3:

> *Those who live in the shelter of the Most High will find rest in the shadow of the Almighty. This I declare about the Lord: He alone is my refuge, my place of safety; he is my God, and I trust him, for he will rescue you from every trap and protect you from deadly disease (NLT).*

Prayer Example:

*Lord, give **Luke** and his family rest. Show **him** how You are his shelter, refuge, and safety. Reveal to **Luke** how You are his God and give **him** courage to trust You. Bless **him** and **his family** with health and protect them from any harm. Cover **Luke** and shelter him with Your love and affection and release Your promises and goodness over **his** life.*

Now I would like you to try this on your own with Psalm 91:4–6:

He will cover you with his feathers.
He will shelter you with his wings.
His faithful promises are your armor and protection.
Do not be afraid of the terrors of the night,
nor the arrow that flies in the day.
Do not dread the disease that stalks in darkness,
nor the disaster that strikes at midday (NLT).

_____

_____

_____

_____

_____

_____

_____

_____

_____

_____

Try the same thing with Psalm 91:7–10:

> *Though a thousand fall at your side,*
> *though ten thousand are dying around you,*
> *these evils will not touch you.*
> *Just open your eyes,*
> *and see how the wicked are punished.*
> *If you make the Lord your refuge,*
> *if you make the Most High your shelter,*
> *no evil will conquer you;*
> *no plague will come near your home (NLT).*

_____

_____

_____

_____

_____

_____

_____

_____

_____

_____

Now that you have prayed Psalm 91 over your neighbor, I would like you to find a creative way to share it with him or her. Here are two suggestions: 1) Buy a Bible, highlight Psalm 91, and then tell your neighbor you've been praying that scripture over him or her. Include an encouraging note if you feel inclined. 2) Write out all or a portion of Psalm 91 and include an encouraging word. Hand the letter to your neighbor in person or leave it in his/her mailbox.

I want to remind you that God's Word does not return void. In Isaiah 55:11, God says, "...so is my word that goes out from my mouth: It will not return to me empty, but will accomplish what I desire and achieve the purpose for which I sent it" (NIV). When you send Psalm 91 to your neighbor today, know that the Lord is doing something powerful.

Remember God's Word is living and active. As you release it today, I believe it will open your neighbor's heart and provide him or her the opportunity to encounter the Father.

 CHALLENGE OF THE DAY

Share your hope in Jesus with someone who looks like they need encouragement.

NOTES & REFLECTION

GIFTS DAY

A demonstration of God's power is vital. It is often what opens the door for people to know that God is real and that He loves them. We see this in Acts 9:10–19 when Ananias received words of knowledge about Saul—where he lived, how he became blind, where his house was, and that he was a chosen vessel.

When Ananias received this revelation, he was fearful because Saul had persecuted several Christians, many of whom were executed for their faith. But he trusted the Lord's voice, took the risk, and changed history by the simple act of obedience.

I would like to encourage you that just as God spoke to Ananias specifically about Saul, He can speak to you about your neighbor. Today, we are going to focus on asking the Holy Spirit to give you revelation about your neighbor. This revelation could come through words of knowledge, prophetic words, words of wisdom, or any of the other gifts of the Spirit. As you do today's activation, I pray that revelation floods your heart and that you receive an increase in the power of the Spirit!

In a moment, here is what I would like you to do:

- Ask the Lord to speak to you about your neighbor. Ask, "God, what are You currently doing in _____'s life? Are there any ailments or illnesses that _____ is dealing with?"

- Ask if there are any key words of knowledge or wisdom that will unlock his/her heart. "God, You know _____. Are there any specific words about him/her that will unlock his/her heart to receive You?"

- Ask, "Is there anything the enemy is tormenting _____ with? What is the key for him/her to be set free?"

Write down what He shows you:

_____

_____

_____

_____

_____

_____

_____

_____

_____

_____

_____

_____

_____

_____

Now that you have received revelation, believe that God is already working in your neighbor's heart and speaking to him or her. Believe that He is with you and going before you. Believe the words He has spoken to you!

5 WEEKLY FIVE: MID-WEEK CHECK-IN

Check off the activations that you have completed this week.

- ☐ Prophetic
- ☐ Healing
- ☐ Words of Knowledge
- ☐ Acts of Kindness
- ☐ Gospel

Take a moment right now to reflect upon Days One and Two. Did you engage with anyone? If so, what happened?

_____

_____

_____

_____

_____

_____

_____

_____

_____

_____

Write down any breakthroughs you received.

_____

_____

_____

_____

_____

_____

_____

_____

_____

_____

_____

Ask the Holy Spirit to show you where He spoke to you this week. In what ways did He speak to you (dreams, nudges, impressions) that you weren't aware of at the time?

_____

_____

_____

_____

_____

_____

_____

_____

_____

_____

_____

In 2 Kings 6, an enemy army, complete with horses and chariots, encamped around Elisha and his servant. When the servant saw this, he grew fearful and asked, "What shall we do?" and Elisha answered, "Do not fear, for those who are with us are more than those who are with them" (v. 16 NKJV). I want to encourage you that as you finish out this week, there are more for you than against you! I pray that your eyes would be open to see this.

 CHALLENGE OF THE DAY

Buy something at your local grocery store. As you're standing in line to check out, ask the Holy Spirit for a word of knowledge for the cashier, release it over them, and encourage them as you are paying. This is a great time to be brief and powerful.

GOSPEL DAY

In Romans 1:16, Paul says, "For I am not ashamed of the Gospel, for it is the power of God for salvation to everyone who believes, to the Jew first and also to the Greek" (ESV). How do you think that Paul, an ex-persecutor of Christians, could say that he was not ashamed of the Gospel? I believe it was because he had a firsthand encounter with Jesus on Damascus Road. This profound experience not only cured his blindness but also changed the trajectory of his heart and life, so much so that he later wrote as a prisoner, "To live is Christ, and to die is gain" (Phil. 1:21 ESV). I believe that through this one moment of extravagant love and forgiveness, Paul's shame of persecuting Jesus was completely ripped away, and he was forever compelled to share the Gospel. This is the same Gospel message we also should feel compelled to share, for, "while we were still sinners, Christ died for us."

I have included a section called *Cultivating the Craft* below that lists two different approaches to sharing the good news, using the foundation I shared two weeks ago—that *God formed us, sin deformed us, Christ transforms us, repent and believe.* I hope it will bring clarity and confidence to you as you share the Gospel.

CULTIVATING THE CRAFT

Your Testimony and the One-Minute Message

Your testimony is powerful! Revelation 19:10 says "The testimony of Jesus is the spirit of prophecy" (ESV). This means that when you release your testimony, it imparts faith in listeners that if it happened to you, it can happen to them. Now, here's a simple way you can share your testimony.

- **God formed us:** Find the gold in who God created the person in front of you to be and celebrate it. Here, you are looking for a connection point where you can relate to how God created the person in front of you. Find the gold in people and tell them about the characteristics of what's shining in them.

- **Sin deformed us:** This is where we communicate our past struggle with sin and where we get to relate with people in their brokenness. Here, ask the person if you can share your story with them. If they oblige, share what you struggled with before you gave your life to Jesus.

- **Christ transforms us:** This is the proclamation that Jesus is the one who saves, heals, and delivers us! In this portion of your testimony, share how Christ transformed you and what your life looks like now.

- **Repent and believe:** This is the invitation for the person to follow Jesus. You can say something like, "I believe

God wants to do in you what He did in me. Would you like Him to do that?" If they say yes, you could pray with them and have them repeat, "Jesus, come into my heart today, I surrender my life to You. I give You my past mistakes, my present pain, and my dreams for the future; I give You my life and choose to follow You today. In Jesus' name."

THE ONE-MINUTE MESSAGE

Let's say you were on a subway, and you only had a small window of time with someone. Here's how you can briefly share the Gospel:

- **God formed us:** First, you could say, "In the beginning, all of us were fearfully and wonderfully made. In fact, He **formed and fashioned us** in our mothers' womb and called us His masterpieces."

- **Sin deformed us:** Then you could say, "But then this thing called **sin** happened and it caused us to bend towards selfishness and pride."

- **Christ transforms us:** Next, you could say, "But here is the **good news**. Jesus came and died on a cross so that we don't have to live that way anymore."

- **Repent and believe:** Finally, you get to **invite the person to receive Jesus.** You could ask, "Is there anything today that is holding you back from receiving the gift of salvation?"

After you put this book down today, go to an empty room, relax, and practice sharing your testimony as well as the one-minute message. As you're doing this, envision your neighbor in front of you, receiving what you have to say.

 CHALLENGE OF THE DAY

Ask the first sick or injured person you see if you can pray for them. If you find an opening, share the one-minute message with them.

NOTES & REFLECTION

ENCOUNTER DAY

For the last couple of weeks, we covered two of the Three Rs from Chapter Five: ready and relevant. This week we're going to cover the last R: revelatory. Whether you have known your neighbor for a week or for many years, one piece of revelation from the Lord can build an instant connection that can change the course of his or her life forever.

Right now, take 10 minutes to reflect upon the last few days when you stirred up compassion and asked the Lord for His word, power, and a way to share the Gospel with your neighbor. See if the Lord is highlighting a revelation for your encounter with that person today.

Write here what Holy Spirit gives you:

_____

_____

_____

_____

_____

_____

_____
_____
_____
_____
_____
_____
_____
_____
_____
_____
_____
_____
_____
_____
_____
_____

Being intentional speaks volumes. If you're going to have your neighbor over for coffee, a meal, or dessert, make sure to make the experience amazing. Be intentional with your preparations, host with excellence, and create an atmosphere around your house where His peace can land.

📅 CHALLENGE OF THE DAY

Find someone sick or injured at work or school today. After you pray for them, see if you can find a way to share your testimony with them.

NOTES & REFLECTION

WEEK 3: DAY 6

INTERCESSION DAY

There has never been a move of God that was birthed without prayer, and you are a move of God to your neighbor. I believe that as you pray today the seeds you planted yesterday will take root, faith will blossom in that person's heart to know Him, and God will encounter their whole household with His love and goodness.

In Acts 16:31, when Paul and Silas worshipped in prison, the doors flew open and the jailer, fearing that his prisoners had escaped, drew out his sword to take his own life. Paul, knowing this, called out to him and told him they were all still present. That is when the jailer saw God was moving and so he called out, "What must I do to be saved?" Long story short, the jailer received Jesus and was baptized, as well as his whole household.

The simple act of worship can lead your neighbor and his/her household to salvation. As you worship and pray for your neighbor and their family today, ask that God would encounter them in such a way that they too would cry out, "What must I do to be saved?"

In a moment, I would like you to take 15–20 minutes to do this:

- Get into a quiet place, like your car or room.

- Close your eyes and envision your neighbor. Take your time and envision his/her face.

- Imagine the enemy has imprisoned him/her and has chained them.

- Start worshipping over him/her; fix your eyes on Jesus and tell Him how much you love Him. Exalt and magnify Him. Do this over and over again.

- Imagine your neighbor's chains breaking off one by one. The prison doors open and he/she starts to worship with you.

- Envision seeing him/her whole. Watch as his/her torment ceases and depression dissipates, as he/she is now saved, full of life, complete, and restored.

- Now hug him/her and welcome him/her into the Kingdom.

Now that you're back, ask God for a key or two that would open your neighbor's heart in your follow-up tomorrow.

Write what He shows you on the next page.

_____

_____

_____

_____

_____

_____

_____

_____

_____

_____

_____

_____

_____

_____

_____

_____

_____

_____

_____

_____

📅 CHALLENGE OF THE DAY

Pray for your mail carrier. Write an encouraging word from the Lord
and put it in the mailbox.

FOLLOW-UP DAY

In 1 Corinthians 3:7-9, Paul says, "It's not important who does the planting, or who does the watering. What's important is that God makes the seed grow. The one who plants and the one who waters work together with the same purpose. And both will be rewarded for their own hard work. For we are both God's workers. And you are God's field. You are God's building" (NLT).

Much like gardeners, disciplers plant seeds, water soil, and tend their crop on a consistent basis. They tend to their field and then watch their seedlings grow miraculously through the wonderful grace of God. However, what disciplers sow isn't vegetation. What they actually sow are seeds of the Spirit.

When we follow up with people to share God's Word, to encourage, and to edify on a continual basis, we are tending to God's harvest. Much as we cannot see the root system of a tree, we do not often perceive what's actually developing in the hearts of the people we care for.

Follow-up, then, is essential for the seeds you've sown in the lives of the people around you. It drives the seeds deep into the soil of their hearts and fertilizes what the Lord is doing in them. It's teamwork. We bring what we have, and God brings the increase.

Here are some tips for what following up with your neighbor could look like this week. As you read through these ideas, think of what God can do in one moment.

- Reach out through text, phone call, or knocking on their door and invite your neighbor out to another coffee or over for another meal.

- Follow up from where you left off. For instance, if your neighbor got healed on Day Five, ask how they are doing. If you got a word of knowledge about one of their family members and prayed for them, find out how they are.

- If they wanted nothing to do with you and the conversation didn't go anywhere the first time, find a way to be kind, say hello, and connect in a practical way. For instance, you can bake them cookies. Or you can maximize the season you're in and bring them pumpkin pie during the fall season or fruit in the summer.

- Engage in things that interest them. Comment on their nice car if you know they're into cars or their lawn if they manicure it often. Just celebrate who your neighbor is.

- If they are working on a project around their house, or if you see a need that they have, see if you can learn from them or lend strength to them.

Now, take a moment to reflect on the revelations the Lord has given you about your neighbor this week. Then ask Him to show you the best way to follow up with them. Write what He shows you:

_____

_____

_____

_____

_____

_____

_____

_____

_____

_____

_____

_____

CHALLENGE OF THE DAY

Call a family member who you have a hard time with. Check in, *listen,* and give an encouraging word.

ENCOURAGEMENT & REFLECTION

Jesus instructed His disciples to pray for laborers to go into the harvest, and now you are the answer to their prayers! In John 4 He promises us that the harvest is ripe. I believe the Father is very pleased with the yes in your heart to answer the call to share the Gospel.

As you continue to reach out to your neighbors, lean into the moments and watch the Lord touch them with His love. I believe with all my heart that He is already working in their lives!

Here are some additional ways you can impact your neighbors:

- Find out when their anniversaries or birthdays are and celebrate them.
- Once a month, choose a neighbor to have over for dinner.
- Watch a sporting event with a neighbor or have a barbecue and invite them over.
- Ask your neighbor to share their story with you.
- Go out of your way to warmly welcome new neighbors that

move into the community. Bake them something, take them a small gift, etc.

Now, I would like you to take a few moments to answer these questions:

In what ways is evangelism becoming more natural to you?

_____

_____

_____

_____

_____

_____

_____

_____

What fears, if any, do you feel you still need to overcome? Ask the Holy Spirit how you can overcome them, and then write His answer on the lines below.

_____

_____

_____

_____

_____

_____

_____

_____

In the last three weeks, who was your favorite person to minister to: your family member, your coworker/friend, or your neighbor? Why do you think that is?

_____

_____

_____

_____

_____

_____

_____

_____

_____

If your neighbor or friend wasn't saved, healed or delivered, take five minutes to ask the Holy Spirit, "Are there any keys that I could have released to see him/her saved, healed, or delivered?" Write His answers here:

_____

_____

_____

_____

_____

_____

_____

_____

_____

_____

⑤ WEEKLY FIVE

Check off the activations that you have completed this week.

- ☐ Prophetic
- ☐ Healing
- ☐ Words of Knowledge
- ☐ Acts of Kindness
- ☐ Gospel

What was your greatest breakthrough this week of the five? What was your greatest challenge?

_____

_____

_____

_____

_____

_____

_____

_____

_____

_____

_____

_____

_____

_____

Ask the Holy Spirit how you can follow up with someone from your Weekly Five this week. Write down what He shows you.

_____

_____

_____

_____

_____

_____

_____

_____

_____

_____

_____

_____

_____

_____

_____

_____

_____

_____

_____

_____

_____

_____

_____

_____

_____

_____

_____

NOTES & REFLECTION

//////////

WILDCARD

WEEK 4

For the last three weeks, we have been riding the wave of impacting our families, coworkers/friends, and neighbors to follow Jesus' mandate of being *"witnesses both in Jerusalem, and in all Judea and Samaria..."* This week, we're going to focus on the last portion of this mandate: *"even to the remotest part of the earth."* As you go out this week, know that you can impact the world right where you are through the unsuspecting people the Lord highlights to you. These people who the Lord draws us to spontaneously are what I like to call wildcards— people like your mailman, your hairdresser, or the businessman reading the newspaper on your morning commute.

This week is meant to be spontaneous, yet intentional. So, get ready to have some fun!

COMPASSION DAY

This week, I want you to go on a new adventure with the Holy Spirit. Jesus promises in John 4:35 that the harvest is ripe. There are ripe people around you today, and I believe God is going to reveal one for you to pray for. This is exactly what the wildcard week is about. It's you lifting up your eyes and looking for the unsuspecting person the Lord moves you to connect with. The wildcard could be the librarian at your college, the student sitting next to you at the coffee shop, or the elderly lady who walks her dog every morning at 7:15 a.m. I believe the Lord will highlight to you someone like this today.

A couple of years ago, as I was checking out my groceries at the store, the Lord moved my heart with compassion for the store security guard. When I asked her if she needed prayer, she looked at me in shock and asked me to step outside for a moment. That's when she burst into tears and began pouring her heart out about the difficult season her family was experiencing. So I prayed for her, and the peace of God immediately filled her heart. For the next couple of weeks, I followed up with her, helping her with groceries, furniture, and Christmas presents. It's amazing how a moment of compassion can lead to a life-changing encounter!

Before you take off today, I would like you to take 10–15 minutes to:

- Envision the people you see throughout your day—the people around you as you commute to work, work out at the gym, go on your grocery store run, and eat at your lunch stop. As you do this, choose the one who moves your heart with compassion.

- Turn on some worship music and spend some time getting His heart for that person. As you do, pray for them, that His favor and goodness would overwhelm them this week.

Write down what He shows you for them:

_____

_____

_____

_____

_____

_____

_____

_____

_____

_____

_____

_____

WEEKLY FIVE

Again, the goal of the Weekly Five is to check off all five of these activations—**healing, prophecy, acts of kindness, words of knowledge,** and **the Gospel**—by Day Seven. On Days Three and Seven, we will have a debrief session with you to check your progress and encourage to you.

⑤ WEEKLY FIVE

Check off the activations that you have completed this week.

☐ Prophetic
☐ Healing
☐ Words of Knowledge
☐ Acts of Kindness
☐ Gospel

Right now, ask the Holy Spirit for eyes to see the ones around you who may need healing, a prophetic word, an act of kindness, a word of knowledge, or the Gospel shared with them. You may feel moved with compassion to share the good news with your boss, or you may get stirred to bring hope to someone as you're having a night out with your friends. Just lean in and continue to talk with the Holy Spirit throughout the week.

In Acts 13, Paul and Barnabas were persecuted as they spread the Gospel throughout Pisidian Antioch. But then the Bible says, "And the disciples were continually filled with joy and with the Holy Spirit" (v. 52 NASB). I declare over you that no matter what resistance you have felt over the last three weeks, you will be filled with overwhelming joy and a fresh baptism in the Holy Spirit! I declare over you that you are victorious!

CHALLENGE OF THE DAY

Find or buy a stocking cap, blanket, and/or pair of gloves, and give them to someone in need at some point in your day (in hot weather, buy and give away a cold drink instead). Then ask the Holy Spirit if there's any other way you could minister to the person.

NOTES & REFLECTION

_____

_____

_____

_____

_____

_____

_____

_____

_____

_____

_____

WORD DAY

Psalm 119:105 says, "Your word is a lamp to my feet and a light to my path" (ESV). I want to encourage you that a simple word from the Lord can illuminate the path of the one you've been praying for. You may not know what your "wildcard" has been going through, but when you speak a word from the Lord, it illuminates a path for them to see Jesus and know that He is real.

Right now, take 10-15 minutes to pray and declare Psalm 23 over your wildcard. Don't rush through the scripture. Engage with it until you feel the Father's heart for that person and pray for them.

Psalm 23

> *The Lord is my shepherd,*
> *I shall not want.*
> *He makes me lie down in green pastures;*
> *He leads me beside quiet waters.*
> *He restores my soul;*
> *He guides me in the paths of righteousness*

For His name's sake.

Even though I walk through the valley

of the shadow of death,

I fear no evil, for You are with me;

Your rod and Your staff, they comfort me.

You prepare a table before me in the

presence of my enemies;

You have anointed my head with oil;

My cup overflows.

Surely goodness and lovingkindness

will follow me all the days of my life,

And I will dwell in the house of the Lord forever (NASB).

Now, write down what you feel the Father wants to release to your wildcard:

_____

_____

_____

_____

_____

_____

_____

_____

_____

_____

_____

_____

_____

In Matthew 21:22, Jesus says, "And all things you ask in prayer, believing, you will receive" (NASB). Jesus promises us that He hears us and answers our prayers when we ask Him in faith.

Be encouraged that your prayer is powerful!

 CHALLENGE OF THE DAY

Who do you know that needs a miracle today? Contact that person and ask if you can pray for them.

GIFTS DAY

In our environment, we often say, "People are just one encounter away from surrendering their life to the Lord." Paul says in 1 Corinthians 14:24-25, "But if all prophesy, and an unbeliever or outsider enters, he is convicted by all, he is called to account by all, the secrets of his heart are disclosed, and so, falling on his face, he will worship God and declare that God is really among you" (ESV).

Prophecy is powerful! As we can see from the passage, it can cause an unbeliever to become convicted, fall on his face, and worship God in an instant! This can happen with all the gifts of the Spirit too.

In a moment, here is what I would like you to do:

- Ask the Holy Spirit for fresh revelation about your wildcard, for clear prophetic words that will allow them to know that the Lord knows them and sees the desires of their heart.

- Ask Him for words of knowledge about any conditions they may have that require healing.

- Ask the Lord to release to you words of wisdom, the gift of faith, working of miracles, and all the other gifts so that your wildcard can experience His goodness.

- Now ask Him how you can share these gifts with your wildcard.

- Write down what He shows you.

_____

_____

_____

_____

_____

_____

_____

_____

_____

_____

_____

_____

This is the day to pray for clear revelatory power to bring to your wildcard. The Bible says that signs and wonders will follow those who believe (Mk. 16:17-18), so releasing what God gives you can be a sign that makes them wonder, "How does this person know this about me? It has to be God." Words like these bring people into an understanding that Jesus is the only living and true God. It shows them that He is real and that He knows them and loves them.

5 **WEEKLY FIVE: MID-WEEK CHECK-IN**

Check off the activations that you have completed this week.

☐ Prophetic
☐ Healing
☐ Words of Knowledge
☐ Acts of Kindness
☐ Gospel

Take a moment right now to reflect upon Days One and Two. Did you engage with anyone? If so, what happened?

_____

_____

_____

_____

_____

_____

_____

_____

_____

_____

_____

_____

_____

_____

_____

Write down any breakthroughs you received.

_____

_____

_____

_____

_____

_____

_____

_____

_____

_____

_____

Ask the Holy Spirit to show you where He spoke to you this week. In what ways did He speak to you (dreams, nudges, impressions) that you weren't aware of at the time?

_____

_____

_____

_____

_____

_____

_____

_____

_____

_____

_____

In Matthew 25:21, Jesus shares the Parable of the Talents, a story in which three servants are given a sum of money to bring back to their master with interest. To the first servant, the master shares his contentment. He says, "Well done, good and faithful servant. You have been faithful over a little; I will set you over much." The Lord sees what you have sown this month. He sees your faithfulness and determination to steward what He's given you, and I know that He is pleased. Right now, I want you to close your eyes and envision Jesus standing in front of you, saying, "Well done, good and faithful servant. You have been faithful over a little; I will set you over much" (ESV). Let those words wash over you as you embrace His pleasure.

 CHALLENGE OF THE DAY

Go on social media and see who has a birthday this week. Choose one person from the list and ask God for a prophetic word you can give them, then send it. If you do not have social media, look to see whose birthday is listed on your phone or day planner. Give the person you find a prophetic word via text or phone call.

WEEK 4: DAY 4
GOSPEL DAY

A.W. Tozer said, "People on earth hate to hear the word 'repent.' Those in hell wish they could hear it just once more." Repentance is a gift from the Lord and the key to salvation! On the next page, I want to give you some keys on how to release this gift.

CULTIVATING THE CRAFT

Inviting People into a Relationship with Jesus

Okay, so the person you've been ministering to has encountered God and tells you they're ready to receive Jesus. You want to lead them through a prayer, but you don't know what to say.

A simple way to lead someone to repentance is through something I learned from Reinhard Bonnke called "the ABCs of the Gospel." It stands for *admit, believe,* and *confess.*

- **Admit you are a sinner:** Admitting that you're a sinner is admitting that you have made mistakes and that you need a Savior. In other words, it's admitting that you've been infected with a sinful nature that bends you towards selfishness, pride, and perversion, and that you need to make things right.

- **Believe:** Believing is trusting that Jesus is the one true living God, because when He died, He was resurrected for your sake. Unlike Buddha or Muhammad, who stayed in the grave, Jesus came back to life in glory, just as He prophesied! This is what you want to communicate as you anchor people in their newfound faith.

- **Confess:** Confessing is declaring that Jesus is Lord. It's posturing your heart in humility, surrendering your life to Him and confessing that He is your master and the One to whom you have given your allegiance. No longer are you your own governor. Through confession, you establish Jesus as the King of your life.

Prayer Example:

Admit: "God, I admit that my mistakes have separated me from You. I acknowledge that my way is not working and that I need You. Thank You that I don't have to do this alone anymore."

Believe: "Jesus, I thank You for dying on the cross for me. Thank You that Your perfect blood washed my sins away and that You stood in my place and took the punishment I deserved. I believe that as You rose from the dead, You gave me a new life."

Confess: "Jesus, I surrender my life to You and make You the Lord of my life! From this moment on, I choose to follow You. Teach me Your ways and fill me with Your Spirit."

Romans 10:9-10 says, "...if you confess with your mouth Jesus *as* Lord, and believe in your heart that God raised Him from the dead, you will be saved; for with the heart a person believes, resulting in righteousness, and with the mouth he confesses, resulting in salvation" (NASB). As you step out to lead your wildcard to Jesus this week, remember it's as easy as ABC.

CHALLENGE OF THE DAY

Invite someone who is unsaved to attend church with you this weekend.

NOTES & REFLECTION

ENCOUNTER DAY

This is your last encounter day of the book, and Jesus saves the best wine for last! As you prepare to meet your wildcard today, expect an outpouring of His Spirit.

Today, I want you to go out with confidence and assurance, knowing that you have been equipped these past three weeks. You are ready, relevant, and revelatory!

Now, I want you to keep in mind that your encounter this week may look different than your meeting with your family, coworker, or neighbor. If your wildcard is your mailman, you may only have a three-minute window to share what God has given you. If it's your barber, you may be sharing as you get your hair cut. If it's your grocery clerk, you may be asking if you can give them encouragement on their break. Whatever your circumstance, I know that God has empowered you to encounter them with His love.

Let's take a moment now to stir up some faith! Say these declarations out loud with me:

- My words bring freedom!
- The Spirit of the Lord is upon me to proclaim the good news.
- Today is a divine appointment for _____ to encounter God's love.
- When I take risks, God shows up.
- My presence illuminates darkness. I am the light of the world!
- I am bold and courageous. My confidence in God is greater than the fear of man!
- His love and peace guide me. There is no pressure to perform.
- There are more for me than against me. Angels are by my side.
- God, Your heart is that _____ should not perish but have eternal life.
- Today is the day: Salvation, healing, and deliverance are at hand!

Take 10 minutes now to write everything the Lord has spoken to you over the past four days—your compassion, your scriptures, your prophetic revelations, and your key Gospel message. Take some time with the Lord, thank Him for speaking to you, and celebrate the opportunity you have to share His heart.

_____

_____

_____

_____

_____

_____

_____

_____

_____

_____

_____

_____

_____

_____

_____

_____

_____

_____

_____

_____

_____

_____

As you go out to minister to your wildcard, I bless you to go with confidence to know the Lord is with you. I pray that all the words you received this week will be confirmed through miracles, signs, and wonders today! (Mk. 16:20).

📅 CHALLENGE OF THE DAY

Ask someone, "Have you ever experienced the power of God?" If they say "yes," ask them to share their story. If they say, "no," ask them if they would like to experience it and then pray for the power of God to touch them.

INTERCESSION DAY

Giving thanks for what God has done brings breakthrough. In Matthew 14:13-21, a crowd followed Jesus to a desolate place. As evening dawned, He instructed the disciples to give them something to eat, despite having only five loaves and two fish. But He took their five loaves and two fish, gave thanks, and the entire crowd of over five thousand people ate and were satisfied.

I want to encourage you that there is power in thanksgiving, and that as you give thanks, God brings the increase. Give thanks for the little and watch Him multiply what you have.

Take a moment right now to give thanks for:

- The revelations received this week.
- The seeds you sowed yesterday.
- The breakthrough that happened, whether large or small.
- The love of God you were able to pour out and demonstrate.
- The heart of compassion you received for this person.

Even if yesterday didn't go as expected, I believe your thanksgiving will open the gates to increase—that your wildcard will encounter Him more and experience more of His goodness. That being said, begin giving Him thanks for:

- The opportunity to be His hands and feet.
- The wisdom you gained from your experience.
- Jesus' faithfulness to see your wildcard saved, healed and delivered.

Take a moment to pray into your encounter yesterday and ask the Lord what you could share tomorrow as you touch base with your wildcard. Was there a revelation you received this week that you were not able to share yesterday?

Write anything He shows you for your point of connection tomorrow:

_____

_____

_____

_____

_____

_____

_____

_____

_____

_____

_____

_____

_____

_____

_____

_____

_____

_____

_____

_____

_____

_____

_____

_____

_____

_____

_____

_____

_____

_____

_____

_____

📅 CHALLENGE OF THE DAY

1) Go into your city with a friend who wants to grow in sharing the Gospel, and 2) find a group of three or more people to share your testimony with. 3) If you can, preach the good news and invite them to receive Jesus.

FOLLOW-UP DAY

Remember that people are people, not projects. Being faithful with the small things demonstrates to people that you care. It also demonstrates that you value what the Lord has entrusted you with.

Do you remember who reached out to you when you were first saved? Did they pray for you and follow up with you? If you can remember and your experience was positive, you know how much it meant to you. But if your experience was negative, I'm sure you can imagine how much good follow up would have benefited you.

When you reach out to your wildcard today, here is what I'd like you to do:

- Share what you received from God yesterday. If you had a short interaction with your wildcard, take the time to finish up your thoughts/encouragements/prophetic words.

- If they wanted nothing to do with you and the conversation didn't seem to go anywhere on encounter day, shake off any rejection you might feel and look for windows to display God's kindness. God will bring the increase to the seeds you sow in faith.

Now, take a moment to reflect on the revelations the Lord has given you about your wildcard this week. Then ask Him to show you the best way to follow up with that person. Write what He shows you:

_____

_____

_____

_____

_____

_____

_____

_____

_____

_____

_____

_____

_____

_____

_____

_____

_____

_____

_____

_____

_____

_____

CULTIVATING THE CRAFT

Discipleship

The Lord has given us a Great Commission to "Go and make disciples" (Matt. 28:19–20). Many times, believers think that being a Christian means being a good person and going to church, but the Bible makes it clear that we are called to change the world, even if it's one person at a time. We need to make disciples!

Say you just led someone to Jesus, and the Holy Spirit moves you to take that person under your wing. Where and how should you begin? Below are two tips that my friend, Chris Overstreet, and I have used to see transformation in our neighborhoods.

1. **Disciple as you go.** Discipleship flows from doing life with the ones you are discipling. For this reason, spending time with new believers doesn't have to be an extra thing or an inconvenience. One of my big keys to creating a discipleship lifestyle is to bring people along with me as I go. This looks like asking people to come to the grocery store or gym with me. Or it looks like working on a project together, such as fixing cars or bikes, cleaning yards, or helping someone find a job. As great as it is to invite new believers over for a traditional Bible study, I believe that some of the best discipleship comes from what Jesus said to His disciples: "Follow me." As people follow us, they see how we respond to situations, overcome challenges, and love God. I have five children, and much of what I

teach them isn't taught; it's caught in our time together. Also, by inviting people into your everyday life, you will find windows to teach the Word, equip new believers in Kingdom life skills, and demonstrate a lifestyle of worship and prayer.

2.   **Learn, Do, Teach.** Discipleship is as easy to remember as *learn, do, teach.* It's like learning how to fish. First, you watch a fisherman catch fish by baiting his line with the right lure and throwing it out. Next, you bait your own line, read the waters, and catch fish for yourself. And last, you teach others how to catch fish. Through the Gospel accounts, we see this is how the disciples learned from Jesus. They first watched Jesus demonstrate the Kingdom; second, they demonstrated the Kingdom themselves; and last, they taught others how to demonstrate the Kingdom. So what exactly do you do as one who disciples? You demonstrate the Kingdom and live such an authentic life that new believers want to *learn* what you're doing, *do* what you're doing, and *teach* others how to do what they're doing.

CHALLENGE OF THE DAY

Treat yourself to a meal at a restaurant to celebrate completing the activation book. Bless your server with an extravagant tip, tell them how generous God has been to you, and share the Gospel with them.

NOTES & REFLECTION

_____
_____
_____
_____
_____
_____
_____
_____
_____
_____
_____
_____
_____
_____
_____
_____
_____
_____
_____
_____

ENCOURAGEMENT & REFLECTION

Your faith to take risks and step out of your comfort zone pleases the Lord. Hebrews 11:6 says, "And without faith it is impossible to please God, because anyone who comes to him must believe that he exists and that he rewards those who earnestly seek him" (NIV). Right now, know that your passion to seek Him on behalf of others is bearing powerful fruit in your life and in theirs. Whether you saw a mighty salvation this week, sowed seeds, or were rejected, God is moved by your faith and obedience. So expect a harvest!

Now, here are a few tips as you continue pursuing wildcards as a lifestyle:

- When you're at the grocery store, ask the Holy Spirit to highlight workers you can encourage and pray for. If He highlights the clerk, be sure to honor his/her job and don't hold up the line. If it turns into a powerful Gospel moment, ask if you can continue to share with them on their break or another time.

- When you're at the gym, encourage people in practical ways. If you see someone pushing themselves hard, maybe wait until they're finished with their workout to share with them how inspiring they are or ask them if they are training for something. Also, if there are people who are more advanced than you in their training, try asking them for advice. This is a great way to build rapport and relationships while getting God's heart for them.

- When you get to a drive-through window, say in a fun and non-religious way, "Have you heard the good news today?" Then proceed to tell them something that Jesus has done for you or quickly share the Gospel. Just make sure to be aware of how you're impacting the business (positively or negatively).

- When you're getting your hair cut, ask intentional questions like, "How is life going for you these days?" or "What's a goal that you want to achieve this year?" Then ask for key words of knowledge that speak into those dreams and release God's heart for them.

- When you're at a restaurant, gather the table of people you're with and write down encouraging prophetic words on a piece of paper for the waiter or waitress. Also, ask the Holy Spirit for words of knowledge to demonstrate His love for them.

Now, take a few moments to answer these questions:

It can sometimes be more challenging to build a relationship with someone you don't know well. In what ways was this week more difficult than the previous weeks? In what ways was it easier?

_____

_____

_____

_____

_____

_____

_____

_____

_____

Ask the Father to show you what He thinks of you stepping out this week. Write down what He tells you.

_____

_____

_____

_____

_____

_____

_____

_____

_____

_____

_____

_____

_____

_____

If your wildcard wasn't saved, healed, or delivered, take five minutes to ask the Holy Spirit, "Are there any keys that I could have released to see him/her saved, healed, or delivered?" Write His answers here:

_____

_____

_____

_____

_____

_____

_____

_____

_____

_____

_____

_____

_____

_____

_____

5 **WEEKLY FIVE**

Check off the activations that you have completed this week.

- ☐ Prophetic
- ☐ Healing
- ☐ Words of Knowledge
- ☐ Acts of Kindness
- ☐ Gospel

What was your greatest breakthrough this week of the Weekly Five?
What was your greatest challenge?

_____

_____

_____

_____

_____

_____

_____

_____

_____

_____

Ask the Holy Spirit how you can follow up with someone from your
Weekly Five this week. Write down what He shows you.

_____

_____

_____

_____

_____

_____

_____

_____

_____

_____

_____

_____

NOTES & REFLECTION

//////////

COMMISSIONING

YOU HAVE BEEN COMMISSIONED!

You did it! You finished the 28-day journey! You said yes to taking risk, you stepped out of your comfort zone, and you let the Holy Spirit empower you to make evangelism a lifestyle.

But this is not the end. I want to encourage you that this is just the beginning of your adventures with the Holy Spirit!

Whether you found the last month challenging or fairly easy, I encourage you to be proactive in your growth. Continue to develop the muscles that you have been strengthening and know that not only are you developing your relationship with the Holy Spirit, you're also developing a powerful skill set that impacts all of eternity.

Here are a few ways you can continue to fuel *your* empowered lifestyle:

1. Do the activations again, but focus on different family members, coworkers, and neighbors.
2. Find a friend or a small group to do the activations with.
3. Instead of doing both the daily activations and the Weekly Five, continue to engage in another month of the Weekly Five alone.
4. Continue to pour into and disciple the people that you ministered to over the last month.
5. If you've received an impression for someone recently, partner with the Holy Spirit to use some of the tools you learned here.
6. Get up every morning and ask the Holy Spirit to highlight people you can minister to.

Before we end, I want you to envision:

- Your family members saved for all eternity, loving Jesus and not going to hell
- All of your neighbors and friends radically transformed through the power of the Gospel
- Your coworkers, one by one, encountering the love of God and getting set on fire for Him
- Your hairstylist, mail carrier, and checkout clerk receiving supernatural hope, joy, and peace

I want to encourage you that all this can happen through you. Again, every ripple effect in history began from a single moment. And I believe your moment is now.

As you continue your journey to live the empowered lifestyle, I bless you:

- With a life of courage, confidence, and no compromise
- With the tenderness to trust the leading of the Holy Spirit when life gets busier
- To walk in joyful expectation and have fun as you continue to take risks
- With increased miracles, signs, and wonders that demonstrate the goodness of our Father
- With faith for the impossible and a supernatural grace to preach the Gospel

Two thousand years ago, Jesus gave a commission to His disciples that He still gives us today. He said, "Therefore go and make disciples of all nations, baptizing them in the name of the Father and of the Son and of the Holy Spirit" (Matt. 28:19 NIV). This is the Empowered Lifestyle! Now, go out and see how the God within you transforms the world around you!

THANKS & ACKNOWLEDGEMENTS

As I wrote this book, I often questioned if I had what it took to see this dream become a reality. But every time I got discouraged, God would send people to encourage and help me along the way. Just one year later, the dream of one book manifested into two!

I want to thank:

My beautiful wife, Hannah. Thank you for walking alongside me on this journey and encouraging me the whole way through!

My five amazing children, Jayden, Adelle, Aliyah, Lilliana, and Emery. May you experience the goodness of God all the days of your life! I love you!

Bill Johnson and Kris Vallotton. Thank you for championing me and giving me an environment where impossibilities are made possible.

Philip Jornales and Mala Johnatty (the dream team). This book could not have been done without you! Your countless hours of crafting my thoughts, editing brilliance, and offering encouragement helped make it a reality.

Solomon Roberts. Thank you for your constant voice of encouragement and support as I stepped out of the boat to try to walk on water in writing this book!

Bethel Church and BSSM. Thank you for teaching me what a revivalist truly is and how to truly value the Lord's presence in my life.

NOTES & REFLECTION

Made in the USA
Columbia, SC
11 January 2024

30333394R00120